THE CANCER

CARD

Dealing with a Diagnosis

Tips for Patients and Those Who Care for Them

Karen Van de Water

Lulu Publishing Services rev. date: 8/30/2016

For Ryan and CJ—
I love you most.

Author's Note

I am hopeful that what I learned along my unexpected cancer journey may in some way be helpful to others. I am not a doctor—nor am I a statistician, historian, biologist, or scientist. I am simply a survivor. I have researched as best I can and believe all information in this book to be accurate. If there is anything that is incorrect, I apologize.

I wish you and yours the very best and send you strength and courage and hope.

As Estha stirred the thick jam he thought Two Thoughts and the Two Thoughts he thought were these: a) Anything can happen to anyone and b) It is best to be prepared.

—Arundhati Roy, *The God of Small Things*

Diagnosis

A really, really old guy goes in to see his doctor. The doctor runs a bunch of tests and comes back. "Sir, I am so sorry to have to tell you I have bad news. You have dementia and cancer."

"Hmmmm," says the old man, ruminating on that unfortunate bit of information for a good while. "Well, at least I don't have cancer."

—joke heard on NPR

There is no planning for cancer. I can't imagine anyone being prepared to hear the diagnosis. I was shell-shocked to learn at forty-seven—healthy, a nonsmoker with no family history of cancer whatsoever—that I had *lung cancer*. A malignant tumor the size of a small hand grenade was lodged in my left lung. Cancer had never crossed my mind as a risk—it resided in the same uncharted realm of possibility as landing on Mars, marrying George Clooney, or winning a Nobel Peace Prize. Okay, so I may have considered nuptials with George, but never did I imagine a cancer diagnosis. My protective cloak of a family tree teeming with generations of longevity stretching back far down the trunk gave me a naive, pompous conviction that I would never face a life-threatening disease. With my diagnosis, I became one of the walking miracles, a survivor living with cancer and a representative of a club no one wants to join—yet membership is flourishing.

Suddenly my life changed forever. I was pummeled physically, emotionally, psychologically, and spiritually. This does not necessarily have to be an all-bad thing—although it also can suck. Here's the truth: it sucks no matter what, at least in the short term. My life became so excruciating I could barely breathe. I felt forsaken grappling with the Gordian knot cancer tied my life into. I can't imagine anyone experiencing the first couple of months as anything except the most challenging, terrifying, and heartrending time yet.

And yet.

I learned of my cancer on that kind of Sunday in February that compels me to stay in my pajamas, pull the comforter to the couch, stoke the fire, and sofa-surf the day away with books and movies and naps while the soup simmers. I avoid venturing out in Massachusetts's infamous winter weather, but the one surefire irritant that will push me out the door is the incessant fingernails-down-the-blackboard whining of a tween. My younger daughter, eleven-year-old Jane, was in a mood. Unless you have experienced middle school daughters, there's no way to fully describe the devastation wreaked by hormones. But if you have, you know exactly what I mean. Hell hath no fury like a sleep-deprived junior high girl, all sullenness and self-absorbed indignation, wielding an iPhone, nail polish, and attitude.

My two daughters and I were headed with my dear friend Stephanie and her two younger daughters to Cape Cod for February school vacation and leaving the next morning, Presidents' Day. I had recently attempted one of Jillian Michaels's workout videos and was then tortured by what I suspected was a pulled muscle and pinched nerve in my back, shooting pain down my left arm. (By the way, whoever made up the plank is masochistic, and the person who thought up prone jumping jacks while in a plank is seriously warped.)

I rarely made doctor's appointments; in fact, on that Sunday, I hadn't seen my primary-care physician in over three years. I was just basically healthy; nothing hinted at my immortality. It is miraculous to me that I went in to get my back looked at; I always trusted that my body could heal itself given enough time, rest, and Advil. I believe I was somehow supposed to go, somehow supposed to "catch" the cancer early, somehow supposed to survive. I have no idea what moved me to go to the emergency room. Jane has insisted more than once that her moodiness driving me from the house saved my life.

She's probably right.

Anyway, some cool hand of fate moved me off the couch and drove me to white-knuckle through a full-on winter storm to Beth Israel Hospital, about a half hour away. My twelve-year-old, Maggie, escaped with me.

The attendant's immediate concern was that my pain was heart related, since my left arm ached. She insisted on pushing me in a wheelchair directly into an emergency room cubicle, where an urgent bustle ensued as I was stuck with cuffs, thermometers, and electrodes. Paper wrappers flew around like ticker tape. Maggie and I smiled at each other, amused by the attention. We knew I wasn't having a stroke or a heart attack and were close to enjoying the medical whirlwind.

Then it ended, and all the medical personnel abruptly left the room. The blue fabric screen swished aside as they made their way to someone or something more interesting or urgent.

Maggie sat on the nearby padded chair, and I lounged on the gurney amid the paper wrappers, with the electrodes still in place on my arm, chest, and head, listening to the hum of the blood-pressure cuff. The staff apparently had concluded I was not having a heart attack.

I remember my nurse being a very nice guy. I learned he was diabetic, but I can't recall how that came up in our conversation. He stayed to clean up all the tissues and unhook me from the machines, although the blood pressure cuff remained, every so often squeezing my arm to remind me of its presence. Maggie and I gave each other a little grin and an eye roll. She texted the play-by-play to friends on her iPhone as I alternated between Candy Crush and packing lists on mine. After a short wait, the Asian equivalent of Doogie Howser came in, dwarfed by his white coat.

"You are not having a heart attack," he informed me. "The x-ray machine will be shut down for repairs in ten minutes, and I am sending you down for an x-ray."

I realized this would take more than the time I felt comfortable leaving Jane home alone, so called her dad, Brian, and asked if he would pick her up and take her and a friend to the mall for some retail therapy. Brian and I were newly divorced, the ink barely dry on the papers signed just three weeks prior to this ER trip. We endured in that raw stage of dealing with the anger and resentment of years of court appointments and trying to formalize how to co-parent.

My nice nurse reappeared and wheeled me past the other stalls of patients to the elevator for the quick ride to the basement and my x-rays.

Maggie still sat in her chair texting away when I returned.

"How'd it go?" she asked in the bored patois of a teenager.

"Fabulously!" I replied with a smile. I checked the clock and texted Jane to let her know we'd be home soon.

Dr. Howser walked in with a clipboard. "Are you a smoker?"

"No." I had already been asked during the preliminary Q and A while they ruled out heart disease. I found it curious to be questioned again but wasn't alarmed.

"What is the name of your primary-care physician?"

"Dr. Cusick. C-u-sick," I replied, expecting a reaction to the ultra-perfect name of my ultra-perfect doctor.

No response. Not even a glimmer of recognition of this great sobriquet. I gave Maggie an exasperated "Can you believe this guy?" look and then checked that Brian had picked up the girls and that they were Abercrombie bound.

Dr. Howser came back. "Where does your PCP work?"

"Mass General Hospital."

I noticed Dr. Howser walk back to the desk, type away at the computer, and pick up the phone. I assumed it had to do with putting in place a follow-up appointment. I felt impatient to be discharged but not worried.

I confirmed with Brian that the girls were happily entrenched in shopping. Maggie texted away, and we watched the hands of the clock slowly march off the minutes. Our nice nurse stopped by and offered beverages, which we declined.

Then Asian Doogie entered and dropped the bombshell. "Your chest x-ray shows a large mass in your left lung."

I was stunned and utterly confused. "What could that be?" I managed. My mind raced to the possibilities. Since I had been told the x-ray machine was due for service, I assumed there was some sort of glitch with the picture. I glanced at Maggie, who was frozen and pale, staring at the doctor.

"I believe it to be a tumor. I would say an aggressive, malignant tumor, given how big it is. I have notified Dr. Cusick, and you will need to go in on Tuesday when his office is open. Do you have any questions?"

You know those old movies where the camera pans onto the person's face and they are alone in a black tunnel, sometimes with kaleidoscope whirls, and there is ominous music? I experienced my own *Twilight Zone* moment, engulfed in an abrupt horror.

My life had fallen off its axis.

The blood pressure alarm beeped, signaling my body responding to my perilous position before it could be fully processed by my brain. (My blood pressure, always within a normal range, would remain high for months, and I would eventually be put on medication to manage it.) I emerged from my trance and focused on Maggie, who was looking at me for answers and assurances I could not give.

Dr. Howser tapped the end of his pen on his clipboard. "Have you had any unexplained weight loss lately?"

"I have lost some weight, but I've been working out and dieting. I expected to lose a little."

"Any night sweats?" he asked as he jotted down some notes.

"Yes, some nights."

"Hmmm, I see." He made more notations. His demeanor made me feel I ought to have known a tumor flourished in my lung, since I'd lost weight and sweated through a few nights of what I assumed were perimenopausal symptoms.

"Look, I'm forty-seven. Should I have been alarmed about night sweats?"

More notes. "Hmmmm? More jotting. "Have you coughed up blood at all?"

"No." I am confident I would have made mention of that particular symptom.

"Well, okay. Any questions?" More jotting, more tapping.

I slowly shook my head, unable to think of a single question relevant to the impending fight for my life.

And with a nod, he was gone.

"Did he just tell you that you have lung cancer?" Maggie asked in a barely audible voice.

"I don't know," I replied. I cleared my throat and tried to sit a little taller, the weight of his words like cinder blocks on my shoulders sending my soul into a slow swoon. "But let's face it—he's not much older than you are, and clearly we aren't taking his word for it."

I later learned there is no way cancer can be definitively diagnosed from an x-ray alone. Although Dr. Howser ended up being right about the mass, he was wrong to voice his suspicions, especially since Dr. Cusick's office wasn't open until Tuesday. Besides the obvious – who gives that diagnosis in front of your twelve year old daughter?

Maggie was petrified. Her paternal grandfather had died of lung cancer. Everyone knows someone who has not survived cancer. We know it's bleak.

"Hey—he didn't even get C-u-sick," I reminded her with a shake of my head and a grin. "What does he know?"

Then we both Googled lung cancer. In my opinion, this is a *big* mistake. It generally is not a good idea to Google any medical ailments, but especially cancer. It is dire. We looked up a few sites and were transfixed by the desperateness of our situation.

The kind nurse came back in and took a look at me. "Well, you look sufficiently shocked," he said with a grim smile. "Look, it's a big mass—about three and a half centimeters. I've seen bigger; I've seen smaller too. You will want to get it removed. Will you come here for treatment?"

"No—my doctor's at MGH, so I think I'll go there." I knew right away I needed to be treated where I was confident I would be cured.

This may have been the conversation when he told me he had diabetes. I can't remember. I do remember I lost it on the way home on those snowy streets. I remember I wanted to keep it together in front of Maggie, but lost it as I told Stephanie I had been diagnosed with lung cancer. It's hard to say out loud; announcing cancer to the universe drives home the truth of the diagnosis. I remember I tried to reach my parents in Oregon and left messages on their phones while my father skied and my mother ski-lodged with my sister. I remember I called my brother, Mark, in DC, who reassured me and was on a flight the next day.

I e-mailed my cousin Julie, a doctor, and told her a mass was found in my lung. I asked her to tell me three reassuring facts and three questions to ask my doctor. Julie told me right away I would be fine, I had a good shot of beating it if it was cancer, and there was a good chance my mass was just some undigested food or an infection of some sort. A bolus that had taken a wrong turn made more sense to me than a tumor. The random thought of a hot dog I ate at the 1982 Benton County Fair popped into my mind as a reasonable culprit to all this speculation.

I reported back right away to my family and friends and heard both relief and an underlying "Of course it's not cancer. You're all worked up over nothing." And I know this sounds crazy, *truly* crazy, but there was a part—a minuscule part, but still there—that needed to be proven right. I was not seeking attention. It's hard to explain. I did *not* want cancer; I just didn't want anyone to think I was being histrionic. I reveled in the newly found serenity with my divorce behind me—I was trying to escape turmoil, not acquire any more.

I remember the drive home that Sunday. The velvet silence of the snow globe of New England back roads offset the disquietude of my thoughts. Brian and Jane, alerted by Maggie, met us as we pulled into the driveway. Brian was worried and astonished, and so much of the anger and frustration of the past few years fell away, as we instinctively knew we would need to unite for our daughters. Brian gave me a big hug and told me I would be okay. It would be one of the last times I saw him before he died a few months later in an accident.

I remember thinking, *What the hell will I do?* I was completely overwhelmed and felt my life had been derailed. I had no idea how to navigate *cancer*. My body had ambushed me, and that pissed me right off. How could it act so ungratefully, given the good treatment I had bestowed upon it for so many years?

I remember I was scared of dying and not being there to see my girls grow up. I thought, *Who will raise my daughters?* Maggie is so kind and clever and capable. In some ways she is young for her age and yet very wise and worldly and responsible. Maggie is the person I would most like to be compared to. She doesn't fit the mold of a young teenager (thank goodness) and has many layers. She simply needs to be able to be herself. Who can be trusted to understand her? And Jane. Wow. When Jane was younger, I felt she was like a supernova and worried she would not make it to adulthood, that she would somehow combust under that much radiance. How could anyone sustain that light? She is funny—not a kid who *acts* funny, but has the gift of being truly funny. Friends would suggest I take my girls on the road and sell tickets to their show—Maggie the straight gal to Jane's irrepressible humor.

They are smart and beautiful—Maggie in a tall, statuesque, "I-don't-know-how-gorgeous-I am" way, and Jane looked like she fell out of a Gerber ad when she was younger and has morphed into a preview of a Ford model. They are strong, which is infinitely better and mightier than beautiful, for it is their strength that will see them through life. Their strength, intelligence, and having each other make them powerful forever. Who could possibly understand and love them and support them if anything happened to me?

They are the best of me. I could not be more proud of them or admire them more. I am also in awe of their ability to knock the wind out of me by how hard and difficult and challenging they can be. They are so smart, so capable, and so unreasonable.

They are why I am beating cancer.

Diagnosis Tips

1) *Assign information gathering to a close friend.* My advice is not to delve too deeply into Internet data. In my opinion, it's best not to get sucked into the dire and often irrelevant articles on side effects and statistics.

Here's an example. A few months after I completed chemotherapy, Jane stepped on my big toe, and my nail fell off. It seemed to take forever to grow back. One afternoon, I browsed big-toenail issues. One possible cause listed was cancer. *Everything* leads to cancer, and everything related to cancer inevitably leads to death rates—which aren't necessarily relevant, but always alarming.

Trust someone to gather the information you need, and ask her to put together the top questions to ask your doctors. My first top five questions were: What stage is my cancer? What is the best way to treat it? Are there any targeted treatments available for my type of cancer cell? When can I get started? How long will it take?

2) *Make certain your legal paperwork is organized* and someone knows where to find your accounts and documents. This is just a nudge to be organized. Get a large binder and put all recent statements, account information, and legal documents in one place.

Here are some of the most important legal documents to have:

A will tells what you want done with your assets and dependent children. This can be an amusing power trip—you may be mad at your aunt Betty for debasing your green bean casserole at Thanksgiving last year—cut her out. Or your cousin Johnny never returned the lawnmower—cross his name right off. Disinheriting someone can be fun. Or add someone who's brought you chocolates and books and good juju, or give the Big Guy a bribe and donate to a church. Hedge your bets and give to a mosque and synagogue too. Whatever you want.

A power of attorney tells who you trust to represent you in legal matters. A spouse or partner, sibling, adult child, or attorney is a good choice. Choose someone with good financial or legal sense if possible. Remember, this person will have access to your wealth and can do with it pretty much as she pleases.

This reminds me—if you have a checking account, make it a joint one so someone else can sign your checks and pay your bills. Add someone to any safe-deposit boxes currently in your name only, and make certain someone has access to your online accounts and passwords. It's important to touch base with your attorney or financial planner if you have one. Also, if you are the custodian of any accounts held for your kids or grandkids such as a 529 plan, call the bank or brokerage and get advice on how to best safeguard their access.

A trust tells how you want your assets dispersed. You can tell your kids they will have to wait until they are thirty to spend your money, or forty, or gainfully employed—whatever you want. The Ferrari they might buy with your retirement funds during their teens and twenties might morph in their forties into a new home or college funds for their own kids. Or you might prefer to imagine them in a sports car. You get to decide.

You can even mandate that they must spend your money on something specific. I knew a guy who inherited money from his grandparents, and the trust stipulated he could only spend it on immaterial things—travel, concert tickets, adventure—the accumulation of experiences, not material goods. I love this idea for all the icing in life it epitomizes.

A healthcare proxy identifies who will make healthcare decisions for you if for whatever reason, you aren't able to make them yourself. This is tricky and may lead to highly contentious family disputes. Assigning a proxy can be problematic. Even if you are clear about when you would want any medical attempts to prolong your life wrapped up, it's an almost impossible call for someone else to make unless doctors say things like "brain dead" or "zero hope of recovery." Even then, stories of people who awaken after years of being comatose may make it tough for someone who loves you to finally accept you're ready to move on.

I was distressed by how many healthcare proxies I signed after my diagnosis, despite already having one. I imagine the hospitals each need a few copies on file just in case. Plan on filling one out a few times. Apparently, this is just part of the reams of paperwork deemed necessary for the successful treatment of cancer.

A living will is like a healthcare proxy, only you write instructions that the hospital must follow, versus having a proxy mouthpiece. You write down exactly when you would be ready for someone to pull out that plug. Of course this can be open to interpretation, so it must be stated as clearly as possible. Avoid words like "suffering" and "incapacitated" and "pain"—these can be ambiguous and hotly debated. Anyone who has had natural childbirth or passed a kidney stone or removed wallpaper may have different interpretations of pain than those who have only suffered through scraped knees or hemorrhoids or cavities.

3) *Insurance.* Dust off your life insurance policies—check that premiums have been paid and the beneficiaries are correct.

This is no time to shop around for health insurance. The carrier you have is required to give you coverage. You will need to have an idea of what will be covered, what your deductibles are, and how much you will pay. Check with your human resources department, and ask if a more comprehensive plan is offered that you could switch to during the next enrollment period. If your cancer is complex, or if you anticipate a particularly long treatment, look into catastrophic coverage. Check your spouse's coverage, and see if that plan is more generous; you might be better off covered as a dependent under that policy. If neither of your plans is extensive, your spouse may consider shopping around for a job that provides excellent health insurance.

If you are single and have to leave your job, you can continue your same coverage through COBRA. You will have to pay the premium (and it will be expensive), but you will be covered.

CHIP is a comprehensive health insurance plan that may be offered through your state for anyone who has had continuous group coverage but is no longer covered. You must enroll within sixty-three days of your coverage lapsing in order to be eligible.

Public health insurance under Medicare, Medicaid, or Veterans Affairs may be available. Reach out to your local social services agency to see if you qualify for any of the benefits of these agencies.

Contact the patient advocate at the hospital; they may know of more resources available to you.

Have a general notion of how this will be paid for. Most insurance companies will work with you on a payment plan if needed. Anticipate doling out most of your deductible in the first month. To put it in perspective, my costs the first year were well into six figures, and I paid thousands out of pocket. This takes a little of the sting out of paying premiums for decades of nothing but good health but is also a hard, unexpected hit on savings.

There will be an abundance of bills, so it's helpful to have a binder or file to keep them organized. If you have someone you can turn this over to, it's a worthwhile task to have taken off your plate. Reconcile the bills each month if you can, so the task doesn't become daunting.

Write down the name and extension number of the insurance representative handling your case. Maintain a record of all calls and a brief summary of what was discussed. Keep a copy of all claims. If there is any dispute in the future, the more documentation you have, the better.

I've included some resources at the back of the book regarding agencies that will help figure out ways to cover your medical expenses.

4) *Review your job benefits.* If you are employed, take a peek at your human resources handbook and review your benefits.

If you work in a company with more than fifty employees, the Family Medical Leave Act requires your employer to give you up to twelve weeks of medical leave. It's unpaid, but you keep your job. Check into short-term disability too; you may get six to twelve weeks covered.

As a cancer patient, you are protected by the Americans with Disabilities Act.

See a benefits specialist, and ask when and what paperwork is needed for coverage. Ask for the coverage to be put in writing to you—either in a letter or e-mail. A paper trail is crucial in case any disputes pop up in the future,

5) *Tell your kids.* They are smart, capable, and tuned in, and will intuit something is wrong. Resources are available to help with this. My hospital, Dana Farber, distributes free kits stocked with books and

games and toys geared to specific developmental ages, the library has helpful books, and so does Amazon.com. I didn't have the luxury to investigate the best way to break the news to my daughters, as Maggie was there for my bombshell, so I'm not clear about the best way to tell kids. I do feel both parents being present would be better, if possible. It might be difficult to talk in a strong, positive way, and it would remind them there are two people who will be there to support them and love them and keep them safe.

Keep the lines of communication open, encourage questions, and be honest.

6) *Get a journal and carry it with you.* This is a steep education, a crash course in cancer. Take notes. I had many sleepless nights, and jotting down random thoughts and questions and concerns helped get some of the worry out of my mind.

Include the names and numbers of your doctors and nurses, all your symptoms, and the answers to all those questions you come up with. A journal is a good place to add your prescription drug information—both the names and the dosages—as doctors need to know exactly what you are taking.

This will be an almanac you take to your appointments and will serve as a great reference.

7) *Eat well and exercise.* I know, I know, it's the cure-all for everything. But seriously, your body needs to be as strong as possible. Most of us exercise to get into our skinny jeans and look good in summer clothes, but the real reason to have a healthy heart and strong body becomes blatantly obvious facing surgery and chemotherapy. This is the real reason—to give yourself the best possible chance of the best possible outcome.

Have an information gatherer find the foods and herbs and teas that best combat your illness. Give a few new recipes a try. I eventually got a juicer so I could ingest great combinations of micronutrients in a single sip.

8) *Rest.* Slow down if you can. Better yet, lie down. Along with good fuel and exercise, your body needs to be well rested for your procedures, punctures, and perforations. Get as much sleep as possible; you may need a sleep aid. Take full advantage of having cancer. You now have—likely for the first time in decades—a pass to take siestas, which are completely underrated.

9) *Work with your medical team on scheduling.* If you have a wedding, graduation, trip, or special event on the calendar, ask about the flexibility of your treatments to see if you can schedule around any important dates.

10) *Be confident and positive.* This is hard—and important. Remember there are *millions*, you probably know some yourself, who have been here and have gotten through it. Put yourself in that mind-set. You will overcome this. It will take a while, it will be hard, and it is possible. Focus on your plan. One day at a time. One step at a time.

Breathe in, breathe out. Repeat.

Tips for the Team

If you are part of the support team for someone newly diagnosed, you may feel wary about what to say or how to react—at least that's what some of my friends told me. Relax, because there is no cancer etiquette. You are the torchbearer through this tunnel; simply do what you can to keep the light shining and the pathway clearly lit.

1) *Don't panic.* I required cool, rational, can-do people around me. I was panicky enough myself and craved positive, calm energy. I had to forgo speaking with friends who were edgy and nervous. I understand it may be hard to be confident and upbeat when your friend or family member has been diagnosed. Just keep in mind she is scared enough for both of you and needs the assurances she will get through this, and you will be there to help. Don't disappear because you feel afraid of doing or saying the wrong things. You might start with simply, "I have no idea what to say or do, but I am here for you any way you need me to be." And mean it.

2) *Lower your expectations.* Don't be hurt if she doesn't get back to you or is out of communication for a bit. I sequestered myself with just a chosen few and focused on my day-to-day path. I did not write thank-you cards, I did not return calls, I did not attend functions, and I did not reciprocate carpools. All social decorum hit the pavement. I focused on no more than what was directly in front of me.

3) *Speak up.* A good question to ask is "What can I help you with today?" This is different than "What do you need?" which can be so vast. Keep it specific to the day. Let her know you are running errands or going to the grocery store. Would she like to go with you, or is there something you could pick up? Milk or a prescription or a child? Any library books to return? A doctor's appointment?

It is invaluable to have someone coordinate a calendar; there are many templates online. This keeps meals, rides, and friends organized and is very much appreciated.

4) *Keep the news to yourself.* Be respectful and let her decide with whom, when, how, and what to share.

5) *Do not ask how she feels.* This is an epic battle with cancer. Enough said.

After Diagnosis

It's far more important to know what person the disease has than what disease the person has.

—Hippocrates

The first time I remember being present to my mortality was when I was planning Jane's fourth birthday party. We started birthday parties for the girls when they turned four, and they could invite as many friends as years they were turning. I was reading in bed, and Jane lay next to me, narrowing down her list of preschool buddies for her chosen quartet.

"Are you one of the four, Mama?"

"Hmmm?" I put down my book and scooped her up. "No, babe—you get to invite four friends from school to come to your party."

"But you'll be there too, right?"

"Of course I will, honey. I wouldn't miss it for the world."

"Will you come to *all* my birthday parties?"

"I would *love* that." I gave her a big squeeze.

"Even when I'm your age?" She peered all squinty at me, and I could tell she was imagining herself that old.

"Even when you are my age." Another squeeze. Is there a better gift than a four-year-old?

"Even when I'm *one hundred*?" She giggled and was having fun as she imagined all those future parties.

It froze my heart for a moment. I would not be there. I wouldn't be anywhere. I certainly wouldn't attend the party celebrating my baby's centennial milestone. I immediately thought I ought to stock up on cards to write to my girls that they could open for their seventy-fifth, eightieth, and hundredth birthdays, to let them know I wish I could be there and celebrate with them and how much I love them. It might seem a bit pathetic, but it was the first time I realized I would one day be dead, or maybe more specifically, not alive.

I have certainly thought more about what is next after this life in the time since that fourth birthday party, which had a Mickey Mouse tea party theme. Thank goodness for Amazon. You can find *anything* on that site, including tea sets depicting Mickey Mouse enthusiastically waving from the porcelain sides of miniature cups.

People are afraid of death. It's an unsolvable mystery. Frankly, it's not the being dead part that seems so bad to me. I imagine it will be like falling asleep and dreaming so deeply you are not aware you are dreaming. I would like to believe I would be able to somehow float around a bit and be able to peek in to see what my loved ones are up to from time to time, or to have some paranormal powers to steer them clear of boarding the plane about to go down—or better yet *super* powers so the plane lands safely, or to give them a big warm hug when they are having a bad day, or somehow compel them to go to the emergency room to get a chest x-ray. (I've had quite a few bring up the fact Someone Up There is looking out for me.)

I hope to be pleasantly surprised and wake up from my longest nap in line at the pearly gates with my grandparents waving from the other side of the wrought iron, eager to get caught up with me. My Gramma Hilda will have a platter of warm chocolate-bit cookies, and Poppa Van will welcome me with a chuckle and a bear hug that will leave a slight red patch on my cheek from his whiskers. We will lounge on chaises and hammocks in a wide-open outdoor space with an ocean a few yards away, its smells and sounds carried to us on a soft breeze. We will read great books. It will by seventy-seven degrees and sunny, and we will wear outrageously colorful sun hats and chat away while channels on a cosmic screen allow us to follow all the great exploits of our loved ones on earth. We will remark over and over about the pure genius of our offspring and marvel at their accomplishments and be content to watch them in their happy lives. And despite never having one, I believe there will be mint juleps in tall, frosted glasses, although Poppa Ed will drink a martini in a proper martini glass with three olives and only the faintest thought of vermouth.

I think the fear of not living, versus being dead, is what leaves people unhinged. People are comforted by heaven or nirvana or all those virgins up there eagerly awaiting. Who knows? Even if it is a nothingness, it is not death itself that seems troubling to me. It's the actual not-living part. It's what I leave behind versus what I'm going to that makes the thought of death hard. I don't want to miss out on this life.

Not yet at least.

Considering life brings to light how the little things are actually the big things. Memories of shared sunrises, weddings, babies, sledding, hugs and kisses, Christmases, vacations, sporting events, Easter egg hunts, story times, sandcastles, birthday parties, picnics, canoeing, s'mores, trick-or-treating, sunsets, and yes, even the late-night feedings, skinned knees, terrible two-year-old temper tantrums, dirty handprints, and braces are what come to mind when one finally takes stock of one's life.

So cancer can be sort of a wake-up call—not necessarily a blinding insight into the meaning of life, but a reset button. As Andy says to Red in *The Shawshank Redemption*, "I guess it comes down to a simple choice, really. Get busy living or get busy dying."

Choose wisely.

⎯⎯⎯⎯●⎯⎯⎯⎯●⎯⎯⎯⎯

I am convinced one of the most common prayers thrown to the heavens by both believers and nonbelievers alike is "Please, God, don't let it be cancer." Cancer used to be referred to in a whisper as the C word, the big C, the bomb. It partners with melancholy to make up the first of Galen's four humors—the earthy, autumnal, cold, and dry black bile—and is one of the oldest diseases known on earth. Mummies, human fossils 2,500 years old, and ancient animal bones all show signs of the disease. Our ancestors wrote about cancer on papyrus. The oldest reference from the

Egyptian court of Imhotep was written more than 3,600 years ago on what is known as the Edwin Smith Papyrus. This ancient scroll tells of eight tumors or cysts cauterized from breasts by a "fire drill." I'm pretty sure we are all relieved there have been advancements in that particular technology. Scripts from India 2,500 years old speak of mouth and throat cancers. The ancient Egyptians blamed cancers on the gods and sum up the disease with "There is no treatment."

The term *cancer* originates from the Grand Poobah of All Things Medical—Hippocrates—who named it after the Greek words for crab—*carcinos* (non-ulcer-forming) and *carcinoma* (ulcer-forming). If you remember your high school crib notes, Hippocrates, who lived some four hundred years before Christ, is universally considered the father of medicine and is credited with detaching medicine from the authority of priests and encouraging people to consider disease not as gods doling out punishment, but rather as originating from within the body.

The word *crab* is thought to have been used because the tumors are hard like crab shells and can pinch, are tenacious and hurt, and frequently show tributaries around the mass that remind doctors of the legs of a crab.

A few hundred years after Hippocrates, Celsus, a first-century Roman, wrote a series of encyclopedias with topics ranging from agriculture to philosophy and medicine. His book sections on medicine were rediscovered in 1480 in the Vatican library and are believed to be the only ones to survive. He wrote of both prevention and cures for disease, of eating well and exercising, of good personal hygiene and experiments on animals and humans to help find cures. (Not much has changed, huh?) Celsus translated the Greek word *carcinos* into *cancer*—the Latin word for crab and wrote "After excision, even when a scar has formed, nonetheless the disease has returned."

●———————●

I will admit I spent a fair amount of time freaking out after my diagnosis. *Of course.* Cancer is terrifying. I was at times catatonic. *Webster's* defines overwhelming as: *Very great in number, effect or force. Something that is so confusing, difficult, etc., that you feel unable to do it.* Check, check and check.

I looked up insurmountable: *Of a problem, difficulty, etc. that is impossible to solve or get control of: impossible to overcome.* And impossible: *incapable of being or of occurring.* And lastly I looked up death rates for cancer. There is not one cancer that has a 100 percent death rate that I found. *Not one.* Yes, there are some scary statistics, but there is someone out there beating the odds. Cancer is overwhelming, but it is not insurmountable; it is not impossible.

Cancer can be beaten. *Believe* it.

I wish my diagnosis had come with a list, a handbook, an easy-to-follow action plan to get me right on through to the other side. I wanted to print out a sheet, preferably with no more than ten specific steps to follow, on exactly how to beat cancer. Ideally a few bullet points and a timeframe of no more than two weeks—a month at the outside. I'm busy, so I don't think it would be too much to ask. Our electric pencil sharpener came with an instruction manual; so did our electric toothbrush and toaster. Why not cancer?

Cancer is nothing close to what I wanted from Life's menu, but fate decided to serve me up a big helping of whoop-ass that I couldn't send back. So now what? Deep breaths. Perspective. There are *millions* of cancer survivors out there, and I now joined their ranks. I was in front of what appeared to be an indomitable mountain of struggle and, like Sisyphus, I would be rolling a rock up it time and time again over the next few months.

The odds were not in my favor, and I decided not to pay any attention to that.

It is important to remember that cancer statistics are collected over five year rolling periods to best show trends. This means that the stats we read are at least that old. Now, five years can go by at the speed of childhood, but take a minute and think about what type of technology you had five years ago. Did you even have a cell phone? Was it smart? What did your laptop look like? Biotechnology is moving along just as quickly. There have been remarkable breakthroughs in the treatment and prevention of cancers. Mostly in treatment, because to dodge carcinogenic influences, we would need to avoid the air we breathe, the water we drink, and the food we eat, which is frankly hard to accomplish. I have found only two things considered safe: filtered artisanal water from a spring unscathed by civilization and organic homegrown kale.

I suggest you read *The Median Isn't the Message* by Stephen Jay Gould. In 1982, Gould, a brilliant evolutionary biologist who taught at Harvard University, was diagnosed with abdominal mesothelioma, a particularly horrific cancer. At the time of his diagnosis, the cancer was deemed incurable, and the average lifespan after diagnosis was eight months. He set out to learn as much as possible about his diagnosis. He explains in this paper how statistical distributions are skewed and how the median is not the number to focus on, but rather that right "tail" on the chart that shows all the patients who live way past the average. Gould left the Harvard medical library after reading through graphs and reports completely relieved and confident he had much more than eight months left to live. Indeed, he lived another twenty years. In fact, Mr. Gould did not die of abdominal mesothelioma but an unrelated cancer. He simply *knew* he would outlive the statistic and beat the odds.

And he did.

———•———————•———

Stephanie and I came of age together in Corvallis, Oregon, where I moved from New York in the middle of sixth grade. She was one of the first of my new friends, and we remained close throughout high school, bonding over late-night clandestine exploits and bad boyfriends and an array of teenage issues mostly stemming from low self-esteem. We went our separate ways in college, though not far apart. I attended Oregon State University; she attended the University of Oregon. It just so happened we both surfaced in Boston at about the same time after graduating college. Stephanie has four daughters. The younger two are very close in age to Maggie and Jane, and they have all known each other literally from birth.

Getting to have a friend like Stephanie must be how the Bankses' kids felt after they wrote the ad and had Mary Poppins show up. No matter the number of superlatives listed, the actual being is so much brighter and better and more beautiful than the words on paper. Stephanie looks like a California surfer girl and is smart, funny, capable, caring, a consummate cook and mom—all mixed together with a dash of daring, drinking a cranberry cosmo. I am forever thankful she is ringside in my life and for our formidable history.

Stephanie and I had had a long-running competition over life's curve balls. We would lament about breastfeeding, dirty diapers, marriage issues, weight gain, tweens and teens—mostly the small negative bumps along the way, as there is no need to compete over all the good stuff; fabulous experiences are enjoyed effortlessly. The rough stuff is easier once shared. So we would each taunt the other with our trials and tribulations to see who might have the lower hand. Not far along in my cancer journey, Stephanie called "uncle," saying I had won for life. There was no way she would ever be able to top the calamity heaped onto my side of the scale. We agreed I win the Lifetime Achievement Award for Who Gets to Have the Worst Year Ever.

She is also a gracious loser.

Stephanie helped me put a floor on what I could handle. The night of my ER trip, it must have been around three in the morning, I texted a question for her to find the answer to when she woke up. She responded right away. *What are you most afraid of? What is the worst thing that can happen? I like to put a floor on how bad the situation can get, then figure out a way to deal with that, and go from there. If we can figure out how to handle the worst thing, then everything else is doable.* I texted back my worst fear. *I am afraid of dying.* It took a few moments for the bubble to show on her end. *Death is NOT an option here. You are NOT going to die. I won't let you. What else have you got for the floor?*

Death then was off the table. The floor we decided on that early morning was that the worst outcome would be if my cancer was somehow environmental and one or both of my daughters was also sick. I had been worried right away after hearing my diagnosis and had gotten assurances from my doctor and my daughters' pediatrician. I needed to be absolutely certain my girls were okay and asked both to go in and get x-rayed. Their father took them two days following my diagnosis. Satisfied with their clean bill of health, I knew I could then focus on what I needed to do. My secondary floor item I felt I would struggle with was brain metastasis. Cancer in my lung coupled with cancer in my brain seemed too much for me—a tsunami in the middle of an earthquake. Defining what I would have trouble handling gave me resolve to fight through everything else.

This fight is tough, no question, and some feel their floor is already broken through with diagnosis. For them the idea of cancer is

KAREN VAN DE WATER

insurmountable. Some feel defeated by the shadows cast by baldness, by illness, by cancer. I am not here to judge. We each have to live our own life as we feel best. I was ready to take on whatever I needed to be around to see my girls grow up and to one day play with my grandbabies. I am not going to let anyone or anything take that away from me. That is not to say I didn't experience crippling anxiety, but I felt there was no time for the luxury of despair.

One day at a time, one step at a time; often it is a matter of taking it on one breath at a time.

Some days will be worse, and many will be better. Hold on to the better ones and know when there is a bad one, it *will* get better.

Breathe in, breathe out. Repeat.

Tips for After Diagnosis

1) *Let people take care of you.* More to the point, let them spoil you rotten. This is a win-win. They get to be the righteously healthy, and you get totally pampered. Let them envy your indulgences. Spread the wealth of assignments, tasks, and the multitude of things you do every single day to support your home, family, and life. Better yet, assign a close friend to organize assigning all the tasks for you. There are scores of calendar templates on line that make this relatively easy, and everyone will have a contact person other than you. People want to help, and getting some of the mundane day-to-day things off your plate will clear some space for your medical appointments, siestas, and happy hours. Pass around assignments to anyone willing to take one. This is better than overloading those close to you with managing too much. I wish I had done a better job with this; I dumped too much on too few. Stephanie, my brother, and my parents were my go-to sources for just about everything. In retrospect I would have handled this differently. I would definitely have participated in more happy hours.

2) *Figure out how you're going to keep people up to date with your progress.* You will want to tell some family and close friends in person or by phone. You may send out a group e-mail, start a blog, or use an online service like CaringBridge.com. I didn't mind who knew. It was cancer; it didn't change me. I would have it removed and move on. Remember this—almost half the population will have cancer this century. If your friend or family member hasn't had it yet, there's a pretty good shot one day she'll be right where you are. You're getting it out of the way first. Choose a way that makes you feel comfortable, and start letting the cancer out of the bag.

3) *Start working on putting together your medical dream team.* Ask around, get referrals, and interview at least two different teams if possible. Be 100 percent confident of their abilities and that they will successfully see you through to recovery.

4) *Notify schools that life is going to get hectic.* My girls' school was terrific. My daughters were given some leniency with assignments and (although I never told them) were excused from detention in case they were tardy in the mornings. Teachers can keep an eye out and alert you to anything of concern. Counselors can check in with your kids from time to time to make sure they are doing okay.

5) *Stock your freezer and pantry.* Even though friends and family will be bringing you all sorts of goodies and meals, stock up on some of your family's favorites. There's something comforting about having familiar meals on hand.

6) *Figure out your plan.* I knew I would need to do diagnostic tests and then surgery, likely followed by chemotherapy. Be unreasonable with the doctors and scheduling. Have them work at a pace that feels right for you if possible. It took little effort—simply asking—to have my tests done within days instead of weeks. Some may prefer weeks instead of days. Figure out what feels right for you and then see if you can gently insist the doctors and hospitals accommodate you.

7) *Schedule some selfish time.* You are going to be stuck, stirred, and stitched in the days, weeks, and months to follow. Set aside some time every day—ten, fifteen minutes—and do a little something just for you. Take a bubble bath, meditate, take a walk, ride your bike, lie in a hammock, read an article, something. Try to relax and simply *be*.

8) *Find someone who has been where you are now*—someone you may already know, someone in the community, or someone online. Like seeing the ocean or giving birth or skydiving, this is something one must experience to fully appreciate. Anyone who has gone through cancer never gets past it, and the experiences are ingrained. They will understand, support, and inspire you. You can pay it forward once done with your treatments.

Tips for the Team

1) *Offer to help organize* meals, errands, appointments, kids, cleaning, laundry, pets, or shopping. Whatever may be helpful to take some of the necessary daily tasks off the patient's plate. If the community doesn't have something set up already, there are several good sites with templates online to help put together a calendar. Remember to double check for food allergies or dietary restrictions before starting.

2) *Introduce her to a survivor.* If you know of someone who has had cancer, particularly the same kind, who might be a positive support, ask the patient if she would like the contact information. I found it extraordinarily helpful to be able to talk with veterans about what I was going through, and it was reassuring to know they had slogged their way through and were out the other side and back to a healthy and fulfilling life.

Along these same lines, let her know of the great survivor stories. Please don't mention that your uncle Joe passed from the same type of cancer. Share the success stories. Chances are she knows more than enough of the horror stories.

3) *Pay special attention to her kids.* Offer to drive to lessons, events, school, whatever. Try to include them more often in fun outings or overnights or take them to dinner or the movies. Life at home will be stressful for a bit, and it was very relieving to have my daughters go out and have fun. No one gets more than one crack at childhood, and it's important to enjoy it.

4) *Walk the dog, shovel the walk, or mow the lawn.* There are seasonal and everyday chores that need to be done around the house. Most of us do them on autopilot, but if you take a minute and think through what you do daily, weekly, and monthly, you will have quite a list to offer assistance for. It's nice to be specific: "I will come by Fridays and mow

the lawn; I will drive Billy to practice every Wednesday; I will pick up your dry-cleaning on Mondays."

5) *Send funny and inspirational cards or notes* to let them know you are thinking of them. Send them frequently and for the next couple of months. Disbelief, grief, mourning, anxiety, anger, sadness, fear—these are all a part of being diagnosed. Offset them with a little laughter. Don't underestimate the power of Hallmark.

6) *Gift basket ideas*—The patient probably still feels pretty much the same physically. This first stage is more emotionally devastating. It may be hard to keep focused on the day-to-day tasks like putting together dinner. Look into restaurants near the hospital or convenient to home. Put together gift certificates for dining or easy-to-prepare meals such as a basket with pasta, marinara, parmesan, and some cookies. Or maybe drop off a basket with some fresh fruit or baked treats.

7) *Don't ask how she got the cancer.* It's human nature to want to know what she did to get cancer so we can then avoid it. But that makes it a bit of a blame game. She didn't do anything to deserve cancer. And if she has lung cancer, please, please, please, do not ask if she smoked. It simply doesn't matter.

8) *Tell her you love her.*

3

CHAPTER

Setting the Stage

In preparing for battle I have always found that plans are useless, but planning is indispensable.

—Dwight D. Eisenhower

The reasonable man adapts himself to the world: the unreasonable one persists in trying to adapt the world to himself. Therefore all progress depends on the unreasonable man.

—George Bernard Shaw

In 1810 the population of Boston neared thirty-four thousand, and the city sat on an isthmus, connected to the rest of Massachusetts by a thin strip of land and seven bridges. Much of what we see today was marshland, the streets were cobblestone, the lights were candles or whale-oil lamps, and our fourth president, James Madison, was in the White House. There were only two general hospitals in the United States: the Pennsylvania Hospital (1756) and the New York Hospital (1791). The Massachusetts legislature granted a charter in 1811 to start work on the Massachusetts General Hospital (MGH). Charles Bullfinch, considered the first American-born architect and famous for his expansion and restoration of the US Capitol Building after its burning in the War of 1812, was chosen as the designer. On July 4, 1818, the cornerstone was laid, and September 3, 1821, the doors of the Bullfinch Building opened.

Mass General records show the first patient ever was a saddler who presented with syphilis. The report meticulously noted he contracted the disease in New York.

MGH has been a teaching hospital for Harvard Medical School since its inception and has maintained a reputation as being one of the best medical facilities ever. Dr. Cusick has his office here, and I have been his patient for almost twenty years. Long before becoming a patient, I volunteered at the hospital.

I moved to Boston the spring I was twenty-three, not having a job or even knowing anyone. It had been my plan to hang out in New England and see what there was to see for six months or so and then move to San Francisco. My intention was to return to the West Coast before the Boston winter rolled in. I traded my car to my parents for a round-trip ticket from Oregon, rolled up my futon mattress, and got on a plane. A friend of a friend of a friend had a couch available, and I took a cab to her apartment once I landed at Logan Airport. I stayed there a few weeks before I settled into my shared apartment on Beacon Hill, where I paid handsomely for space in a walk-in closet. One thing led to another, and my six-month visit has stretched to a twenty-six-year residency. I have now joined a long line of Yankee ancestors who consider ourselves New Englanders.

My first job was at the Sky Club—a swank downtown gym sitting on the top two floors of the Devonshire Building, a stone's throw from where the Boston Massacre occurred. I am still astounded that anyone attended my five-o'clock morning aerobics class. I was truly terrible, as my pay grade reflected. I had zero disposable income and volunteered at a few organizations as a free way to contribute and connect to the community.

The volunteer position I held at Mass General Hospital was perfect. Every Thursday afternoon for a few hours, I stood at the reception desk in my salmon-colored polyester blazer, greeting visitors and giving directions to their various appointments. And—the best part—I got to take the wheelchairs up and wheel out the patients after they had been discharged. The patients were always happy to see me, thrilled to be going home, and it was a constant subtle reminder of how to focus on the big stuff and let the little problems slide. This was especially true for me when the kids came in, the cancer patients immediately recognizable and particularly poignant with their bald heads and swollen, beautiful faces.

My brother, Mark, and I went to MGH the Tuesday after Presidents' Day for my follow-up appointment with Dr. Cusick. Mark is sixteen months older than I; we were told we are products of the poor heating in the army apartment my parents were assigned in Bamberg, Germany. Our father spent two years paying back his college ROTC scholarship with service to our country. Dad later got a job involved with setting up international exchange programs for Syracuse University students, and we moved just about every year and a half until settling in Oregon when I was twelve. At last count, I have attended seventeen schools. My brother and I were necessarily close for most of these transitional years and then had the usual sibling rivalry in high school, fighting over the car, the TV station, and bathroom space.

Mark is the quintessential good guy. He is a fabulous father of three remarkable children, and a successful executive in Washington, DC. Mark has been married for more than twenty years to a smart, capable, beautiful woman. I am incredibly thankful to have him as a big brother. His can-do, positive attitude and methodical ways were exactly what I needed in my corner through diagnosis and the oncoming onslaught of chemotherapy. Mark has a way about him that made me feel it was no imposition at all for him to leave his job, his family, and responsibilities and travel hours to come up and hang out with me for days while getting my medical maelstrom handled.

No biggie.

Dr. Cusick was out of state that Tuesday, so we met with one of his colleagues; let's call her Dr. Not Cusick. Dr. NC greeted us and let us know she had reviewed my x-rays, and there was no way to know what the mass was without further tests. She gave a few different, non-life-threatening scenarios and said she would schedule some further assessments in a few weeks' time. This did not sit well with me. Although those other non-life-threatening scenarios seemed much more likely than my having lung cancer, I still needed to *know*. My sole focus was to figure out what my problem was so I could move on to the solution stage. Without the identification of what needed fixing, I was left in a place of a not-knowing imagination I didn't want to dwell in any longer.

"Ummm, that actually doesn't work for me. I really need to know what that mass is and what I need to do about it. I need it removed as soon as possible. What tests can I do right now—*today*—to get started?" I tried to give her my best "let's work on this together and come up with a solution" smile, but I'm afraid it may have looked more like a "there is no effing way I am waiting *weeks* for a diagnosis" smile.

Dr. NC considered my request for a few moments and then wheeled back in her black, round, twirly chair and headed for the door. "I will give Dr. Cusick a call and see what he suggests," she said a wee bit smugly.

"Thank you." I could afford a sincere smile, as I knew Dr. Cusick would understand and light this process up for me.

Sure enough, Dr. NC returned about five minutes later. She sat, wheeled herself back to the small desk, and pulled out a pad and pen. She seemed somewhat contrite, but that may have been wishful thinking on my part.

"Here," she said as she handed me a slip. "Take this down to the ground floor, and they will do a CT scan. Dr. Cusick will see you tomorrow at one to go over the results and schedule your follow-up tests."

"Thank you very much."

And just like that, we were off to figure out what had taken up residency in my lung and how it would be evicted.

The human body has about 37.2 trillion cells, and the fact they cooperate and collaborate to produce a functioning human body is miraculous. Almost all our cells are in a constant state of life cycle, with new cells being made and old cells dying all the time. Our stomach lining replenishes itself every five days, skin cells live two to three weeks, red blood cells live around four months, and our brain cells live our lifetime (or at least the ones we don't kill off partying during our teens and twenties). We learned in biology that cells are the basic building blocks of life; cells make up tissues, and tissues make up organs. Our DNA is the conductor and is responsible for making certain new cells are the exact replicas of the ones they are replacing, and any cell falling short of perfection is summarily dispatched.

We are all, every one of us, born with cancer genes as part of our DNA. These *oncogenes* remain dormant unless activated by some factor—cigarette smoke, radiation, chemicals, bacteria, viruses, or endogenous error. The DNA is then altered, and the aberrant cells start to proliferate uncontrollably.

Carcinogenesis is the process by which healthy cells become malignant cells, and a *carcinogen* is the substance or factor that gets these cellular changes started. They are formed by mutations of certain normal genes called *proto-oncogenes* that control how often a cell divides. In cancer, there is oftentimes an issue with these genes dividing at warp speed—the gas pedal getting stuck in our corporeal vehicle.

Tumor suppressor genes slow down cell division, repair DNA errors, and tell cells when to die. These are the second set of genes commonly found to have mutated when cancer is discovered—our gene replication brakes not working.

So to sum it all up, cancer spreads when either the gas pedal of abnormal cells is stuck and they keep replicating like crazy or the brakes aren't working and they won't stop or, better yet, die.

There are two major types of lung cancer: non-small-cell and small-cell. Non-small-cell lung cancer (NSCLC) is the most common and accounts for 85 to 90 percent of all cases. NSCLC is broken into three different main subtypes depending on the size, shape, and chemical makeup of the cells. The treatment and prognosis is pretty similar for each of these.

- Adenocarcinoma is the most common form of lung cancer, accounting for about 40 percent of all diagnoses, and is what I had. It is the most common type found in nonsmokers, especially women, and is more likely to be discovered in younger patients. This type of NSCLC is usually located in cells that would normally secrete substances like mucus along the outer parts of the lung and is a slow-growing type of lung cancer so is more likely to be found before it's metastasized.

- Squamous-cell carcinoma accounts for 25 to 30 percent of all lung cancers and starts in the flat cells that line the inside of the airways of the lungs, called squamous cells. This type of NSCLC is often found in the middle of the lungs, near a bronchus.
- Large-cell (undifferentiated) carcinoma makes up about 10 to 15 percent of lung cancers. It tends to be harder to treat because it grows and spreads fairly quickly.

Small-cell lung cancer is treated differently than non-small-cell cancer. For whatever reason, it is also referred to as oat-cell cancer or oat-cell carcinoma. It's named after the size and shape of the cells and usually starts out in the bronchi, in the nerve and hormone-producing cells of the lungs, and then spreads quickly. It's usually found after metastasis.

So once a cancerous tumor starts growing, it can be benign (noncancerous) or malignant (cancerous). The mass may or may not metastasize (shed and spread cancer cells to other parts of the body). If the lesion does shed cells, they can be transported in blood or fluid called lymph. Lymph travels toward pooling stations called lymph nodes, which are tiny, bean-shaped organs that help fight infection and are located in the lungs, the center of the chest, armpits, behind the knees, and around the body. The natural flow of lymph out of the lungs is toward the center of the chest, which explains why lung cancer often spreads there first and why some of those nodes are removed and biopsied.

●────────────●

CT Scan with Contrast

Your whole life you go to school and learn lessons you are then tested on. As they say, now is your chance to have the tests and then learn what you need to know. Buckle up, 'cause you're in for some serious schooling.

My education began when Mark and I found our way to the right department down on the lower level of MGH. I filled out some forms and was given a nasty-tasting contrast drink to finish while waiting my turn. I checked in with Stephanie, who had heroically taken all four girls to the

Cape solo. She reported our daughters were taking turns going from the pool to the hot tub while she enjoyed a well-deserved glass of wine and kept an eye out so no drowning occurred.

My turn finally arrived, and I was ushered into an antechamber and told to put my clothes in a locker and put on one of those unappealing hospital gowns. I'm no fashionista, but it's kind of hard to believe no one has designed a hospital gown a little (and by a little, I mean substantially) better than what we have going on right now. A whole lot more people wear them than those designer dresses at the Oscars. Seems an up-and-coming designer could make quite a splash and get her name out there with a snazzy new hospital gown. Let's work on that.

I got to wait again, this time in a small hallway off the main buzz of the CT rooms. I could see into the control room and watched the blue haze of computer images reflecting on the technicians' faces. The woman across from me was wearing a fur coat over her hospital gown, and I found that somewhat distracting. She was on her cell phone, lamenting about yet another scan and wondering if she would catch her flight to New York City in time for some gala happening later that evening.

I browsed *People* magazine. I can tell how busy life gets by how up to date I am with *People*. I never buy one but do admit to reaching for one and reading it cover to cover whenever I'm in a waiting room. The car getting serviced, dental checkups, orthodontists, pediatricians, hair appointments—these are the times I get to catch up on the very important lives of the very important stars. I would know more about who, what, where, why, and with whom in Hollywood than I ever knew possible in the next couple of months of waiting.

Fur Coat went in before me; then it was my turn. The room was sterile with a big, white, donut-shaped scanner smack in the middle, sticking a tongue out in the form of a bed. The technician directed me to lie down, after asking me to remove my necklace please. After checking that I was not pregnant and didn't suffer from claustrophobia, he asked if I had ever had a contrast scan done before. Not only had I never had one; I actually had no clue what I was doing. I was going along on the blind faith I have in Dr. Cusick and trusted he was sending me where I needed to go.

"Well, I am going to set up this IV, which will put a dye into your veins and allow a better image of what's going on in your organs. Some people say they feel a sense of warmth—actually, quite a few say it feels like they are peeing their pants."

"Yikes. I will be happy to know I'm not."

"Also many say they get a metallic taste in their mouth. But it's not that bad. It will only take about ten minutes to get everything I need. I will be right over in that booth, and if you need anything or feel any discomfort at all, just let me know. I will be able to hear you and talk to you through this intercom." He pointed to some speakers inside the tube.

He attached a little butterfly needle to my arm, and I felt warmth as the contrast started entering my vein. The technician stayed long enough to check that I was not having an allergic reaction and then left to escape the radioactive waves about to give me the answers I needed.

I later discovered that CT (commuted tomography) or CAT (computed axial topography) scans have come a long way since being invented in 1972. Originally only used on the brain, whole-body imaging became available in 1976. Back then it took several hours of the patient lying quietly, periodically holding her breath for a single scan (or "slice" as the medical people call it) to be produced—and then days to reconstruct all the data into a comprehensive, readable format. Now, the CT scanner at MGH collects four slices in around 350 milliseconds, completely scanning my entire chest cavity in five to ten seconds. The slices are then put together like a loaf of bread, creating a comprehensive three-dimensional image.

A few patients have an allergic reaction to the dye, and this can be unnerving. The technician was careful to only administer a very small amount and checked carefully for any adverse reactions that are apparently obvious right away. Complications are particularly prevalent in people who are allergic to foods or those who have asthma. I have asthma and am allergic to shellfish. (I still eat shellfish because it's delicious, and I frequently will break out in hives afterward. On occasion, after a particularly gluttonous intake, I will have an asthma attack, which I know sounds ridiculous, and I am more careful to not overindulge now that my lung capacity is diminished.) Some reactions to the dye can be severe, but keep in mind the National Institute of Health gives the chance of death here at 0.0006 percent. That's a lot of zeros. And here's something to consider—one hundred people a year die from ballpoint pens.

Don't ask me how.

I learned a CT scan with contrast is needed because the iodine mixture goes into the bloodstream and circulates throughout the heart and body. The blood vessels and organs fill up with the liquid, and this enhances those areas on the CT images. I was told to drink a lot of water afterward to give the unsung heroes—my kidneys and liver—a hand with flushing out the contrast.

The attendant settled into his booth and asked me over the speaker to close my eyes (not sure why), and the bed gently slid into the opening. The donut started rotating around me as I lay there. It clicked as the technician asked me to hold my breath, for what turned out to be pretty much the outer limit of my ability, and then I heard, "Okay, you can breathe now." This was repeated a few times, and that's all there was to it.

Easy.

I did feel like I'd wet myself. The warmth traveled throughout my body but definitely settled, to make me feel like I needed a change of pants. I also had a taste in my mouth as though I had been chewing on a pocketful of loose coins.

But it's fine; this is not a big deal. Unless you get claustrophobic, then it might be a good idea to ask for some Valium or something to help you relax.

"Hang on a moment, would you? I want to make sure the pictures are clear and we have what we need." His voice resonated through the speaker inside the donut.

"Sure thing; no problem."

It was cool and quiet, and I took a minute to examine the inside of the tube and thought of all the wires and computer circuitry the smooth white casing was hiding—and the answers it already had about my mass.

"Okay, I think we have what we need." He returned and pushed a button, and my bed slid out of the mouth of the donut.

"How does it look?" I was trying to read him, to see if he would give anything away. I was hoping for the "I'm not supposed to say anything ... but you are fine. There's nothing there at all!"

In a well-rehearsed way, with a nice smile that made me like him even more, he instead said, "Oh, I only take the pictures. I don't interpret them. That's not in my pay grade."

"Thank you," I said as I picked up my necklace and hurried back to get dressed and to rescue my brother from the waiting room.

The next day Mark and I were back at MGH to see Dr. Cusick, who reminds me a bit of Ray Liotta, tall and sturdy and a little bit on the rugged side. I once heard it's smart to have a doctor and a lawyer about your own age, as you want to stay with the same counsel for as long as possible. The last time Dr. Cusick and I had seen each other was at the Taylor Swift concert at Gillette Stadium the previous summer. He was there with his wife and three daughters, and I had taken Maggie, Jane, and two of their friends. It was a beautiful night in June, and I happened to walk by him on my way to the bathroom, and he called to me. I went over and oohed and aahed over his adorable daughters and got to meet and say hi to his beautiful wife.

And here we were.

Mark and I sat waiting in an examining room, having a conversation about the size of Africa. My brother is a smart guy, and I remember being especially impressed with myself for winning the bet on the fact that Africa is larger than North America. Africa is an enormous continent, and there are all sorts of cartographical errors in the representation of how big it is. The United States, India, and China can all easily fit within its boundaries. Look it up. It is vast.

Dr. Cusick entered, and I introduced him to my brother. He shook Mark's hand and then gave my hand a shake that turned into holding it a bit as he looked directly at me.

"How are you? What can I do for you?" he asked in a very concerned tone.

"You can tell me I don't have lung cancer."

He took a deep breath and exhaled as he said, "I can't do that. The scan shows a tumor, and we will need to have it taken out. Now there is a chance it's benign."

My shoulders slumped, and I felt defeated as if a safety line I had been hanging on to had been cut away. I felt tears starting to fall. Dr. Cusick handed me the ever-present box of tissues on the desk and turned on his computer.

"The CT shows one mass we should look into right away; then there are two smaller spots on the film, but it's hard to say whether or not we ought to be concerned about them at this point. Would you like to see the scan?" he asked.

I hopped down off the examining table I had been perched on and studied the computer screen as he scrolled down the images of the inside of my lung. It was like a video game the girls might play on their phones. The images spiraled down inside my lung, showing areas I frankly had no idea what I was looking at, and then, right there in the middle of the screen, we saw the mass of my tumor. He went forward and then reversed and went through it again. It was like a ride at Disney—Lung Tunnel, when all of a sudden you drop into darkness and your stomach ends up in your throat and you realize you are terrified.

How had my body allowed this to happen? Why couldn't I somehow push an override button or take my body off autopilot and be able to sort this out and get my healthy, normal body back? One thing I did know: I was not about to give this mass any power. I was not about to let it dictate what my life was going to be. I was going to wage a campaign all about its destruction. This necessitated bifurcating my *self* from my *body*, as the mass was also part of me. I started thinking of going forward as being two different entities—my self, which was going to make it through and was fine, and my body, which needed to be partially dismantled and rebuilt into a healthier, cancer-free body that my self could safely return to.

"I'm going to schedule some more tests for you so we can get the correct diagnosis, and we will go from there. We will need to set up a biopsy and a surgical team to have this removed." Dr. Cusick was all business.

"If, God forbid, your sister had lung cancer, who would you want her to go to for treatment?"

I trust Dr. Cusick, and I doubt he changed his mind or gave me a name he wasn't about to anyway, but in the past, there had often been a slight pause when asking this question, as the doctor imagined a sister or daughter or wife in my seat and what would be best for her.

"I would have her see Dr. Amazing. He is the best thoracic surgeon I know here at MGH. I will call and get you an appointment to see him as soon as your test results are back."

He clicked away at his computer, making appointments for me. "I've got you in for a needle biopsy on Friday. I also want you to have a PET scan done, but these other departments look pretty booked up. Let me make a few calls and see what I can do. Hopefully I can get the rest set up today and will let you know later on when your other appointments are. Any questions or anything I can do for you?"

"No, thank you."

He addressed Mark. "You are a good big brother to come here with your sister. She needs support, and it's so nice to see you here with her. I have a younger sister too, so I really appreciate what you are doing. Thank you."

Then he gave me a big hug and left the room on a mission to get me in as soon as possible for all the other tests I needed. The goal was to complete the picture coming into focus called "What is this mass and what are we going to do about it?"

My cancer dance card was filling up.

Dr. Cusick called me at home that night to let me know that although the hospital in Boston was booked up, he was able to get me an appointment at the MGH imaging facility in Chelsea on Sunday. I would get a PET/CT scan done to put to rest my second big concern of brain metastasis. He also gave me his home and cell phone numbers and told me not to hesitate to call him if I needed anything at all or if I had any questions.

I wish everyone had a doctor like him.

Mark was flying back to DC the next afternoon, and my parents were arriving from Oregon almost simultaneously. As Mark and I didn't have anything scheduled in the morning, we decided to go down to the Cape to have breakfast with the girls and Stephanie. I had been chatting with Maggie and Jane consistently since they left Monday morning, but I thought it would be good for them to see I was okay and still in one piece—practically.

So Thursday morning, we met at a little diner two blocks from the ocean, and I had my all-time favorite breakfast of eggs florentine. We ate way too much and headed out for a walk on the beach. We took some selfies and some pictures of the girls with the ocean as a backdrop. Jane gave me a shell she found, which she said would give me good luck. I carried it with me for weeks—and it did.

Here is my CT scan report:

HISTORY:
Abnormal x-ray or ultrasound—new 4cm lung mass in nonsmoker.

REPORT TECHNIQUE:
CT of the abdomen and pelvis WITH intravenous contrast.

Scans were continued into the pelvis to evaluate for possible metastatic disease.

COMPARISON: None available.

FINDINGS:
LOWER THORAX: A chest CT was performed on the same date. Please refer to that report for evaluation of the chest.

HEPATOBILIARY: No focal hepatic lesions. No biliary ductal dilatation. Thickened fold of the gallbladder may represent adenomyomatosis.
SPLEEN: No splenomegaly.
PANCREAS: No focal masses or ductal dilatation.

ADRENALS: No adrenal nodules.
KIDNEYS/URETERS: No hydronephrosis, stones, or solid mass lesions.
PELVIC ORGANS/BLADDER: Unremarkable.

PERITONEUM / RETROPERITONEUM: No free air. Trace free pelvic fluid, likely physiologic.
LYMPH NODES: No lymphadenopathy.
VESSELS: Unremarkable.

GI TRACT: No distention or wall thickening.

BONES AND SOFT TISSUES: No suspicious lytic or blastic lesions identified.

IMPRESSION:

No CT evidence of metastatic disease within the abdomen or pelvis.

Probable adenomyomatosis of the gallbladder.

Biopsy

Thursday afternoon, my brother handed the baton over to my parents, who arrived within an hour of his departure. I felt ensconced by their being my gatekeepers to all things. My mother researched foods and recipes of every known variety even hinting of being good for cancer patients, and my father organized and made lists in his left-handed cacographic scrawl of appointments and procedures and questions and results. They totally managed the household, kids, dogs, yard, and all errands great and small.

They are an indefatigable force.

Friday found us back at MGH for my needle biopsy. I couldn't help but think those waiting with us naturally would assume I was the one there giving moral support to my parents. It is likely less usual for the seventy-something couple to be overseeing their forty-something kid's medical crisis. Most patients seated with us were baby boomers, with a few from the greatest generation tossed in the mix. I couldn't help but wonder what each was in for. Did they have kids at home to care for? Were they nervous about their appointment? Was it their first, or had they been coming in as part of a routine that shaped their lives and sleep?

We first went down to get an updated CT scan done—this one without contrast—so the biopsy doctor would have the most up-to-date images to plan the needle's exploration of my lung. Then we found our way through the MGH labyrinth to where the biopsy would take place.

My mother was working on a grocery list, and my father was trying to get some insurance questions answered. I was relieved to see an older, Indian doctor emerge to take me back to the operating room. I know it's stereotypical and not politically correct, but I feel Indians and Asians tend to be somehow smarter and more accomplished than average. There is something about Indians that makes me think of wise yogis and sages and transcendental know-how.

The doctor—I will call him Dr. Guru—welcomed us into his "office," and the four of us squeezed in knee to knee so he could go over the procedure. He showed us a diagram on his computer of how the long needle would be inserted into my lung and retrieve a portion of the tumor so they could determine whether or not it was malignant and which type of aberrant cells were taking over my healthy lung tissue.

I wasn't nervous about the procedure. I had a clear path of my journey to rid myself of lung cancer, and this was a step on it. Diagnosis, scans, biopsy, scans, surgery, scans, chemo, scans, and more scans, and more scans. The scans will actually never stop, and life will be lived in three-, then six-, then twelve-month scan segments.

I asked the surgeon three questions. I pictured Jabba the Hutt lounging snugly and bingeing away at my healthy lung. I was worried the needle would disturb it, and like a beehive, agitate the cells and encourage them to seek quieter organs to colonize. I was assured this was not the case. I also wondered if he could vacuum out the entire mass—suck it all right on out through the biopsy straw. No, not possible. Thirdly, I was concerned about my second "floor" issue. I asked if there was any way to determine if the cancer had spread, explaining that I was nervous about it traveling to my brain. My guru studied me, tilted his head a bit, and asked quizzically, "Why are you scared of cancer in your brain?" I told him I didn't understand his question. He repeated himself, and I was at a loss. Why wouldn't I be scared of cancer in my brain? I never really learned the genesis of his question but took away that perhaps I should just concentrate on dealing with what I knew I had on the table.

I learned that if my lung cancer had metastasized to my brain, I would not have brain cancer; I would have lung cancer in my brain. That was a surprise to me. I had thought a cancer cell was a cancer cell, and wherever it was found, that was the type of cancer one had. But not true. Like tourists—if I were to travel to Paris, it would not make me French; still an American, but just in France, soaking up the sights. There are more than a hundred different kinds of cancer, and lung cancer can be in your brain, your lymph system, your bones, your kidney, wherever. Lung cancer often shows up other places, since there are no nerve endings in your lungs, so people usually don't realize there is something wrong until the cancer metastasizes and starts causing noticeable problems. That is the primary reason it is so hard to manage.

"Why would she have lung cancer? She's young and a nonsmoker, and no one in her family has had cancer." My mom pointed to me. "Look at her—she's *healthy.*"

I got that a lot—friends and family were flabbergasted to learn I had cancer. I eat organically, shun fatty foods and red meat, work out almost as much as I should, have an amazing family tree filled with health and longevity, and I seem healthy enough to sidestep most sickness.

I remember being impatient with the question. As far as I knew, there was no good answer to it. I had "bad luck" cancer (as if there is any other kind). I didn't want to spend time on the hypotheticals and the whys of the problem; I simply wanted to move toward solving it. *Why* didn't matter much; all that really concerned me was that cancer had found me.

"Mom, they don't know."

"No, she is the mother. She wants to know why her daughter is sick," Dr. Guru said slightly admonishingly.

Then I got that my cancer wasn't only *my* cancer. Like the pincers of a crab, it had reached out and grabbed hold of everyone close. I remember sitting with what Dr. Guru said and realizing how cancer insidiously worms its way into so many lives, with or without the tumor.

My mother is a strong woman, although more pen than sword. She is softly adversarial and gets much of her strength from the bindings of a fifty-two-year marriage to a steadfast, capable partner. She was the nineteen-year-old beauty queen who married the twenty-one-year-old bespectacled Clark Kent. Theirs is the rare union that grows together as a pair, not individually, like saplings that start out separately but fuse together in a herringbone weave until the individual shoots are no longer discernible.

My mother is the breeze in the sails of their marriage, my father their captain. I imagine my dad wishing she would fan them farther from shore, to uncharted territories and wilder seas. She prefers the safety and calm and quiet beauty of the clear shallows. My dad is content for the most part to anchor in the shoals, but restlessness and wanderlust overcome from time to time, and he heads out on his own to foreign ports to explore and seek adventures and experiences to embellish the tranquil waters of their lives.

I've never really admitted this, but I think it's fair to say for much of my life, I have felt like a disappointment to my parents. They grew impatient with my lack of direction, my inability to live up to my capabilities, my reluctance to embrace responsibility.

Sure, a part of me recognizes I may have had the potential to steer my life in a different direction. Or maybe not. I'm not sure I would have been any happier following my parents' envisioned path for me. I didn't choose a straight course but managed to make my way to a pretty good spot. I am content with my life and what I have accomplished. I've had a great ride so far, especially if you don't count the mistakes, accidents, and cataclysms. I have traveled the world—taking my girls on a ship that circumnavigated the globe and allowed me to cross off virtually everything on my bucket list. I have skydived and been in a submarine; I have camped in Alaska and attended a private black-tie dinner at the Versailles Palace. I have met rock stars and presidents and built homes with villagers in Ghana. I have had a successful career; I have been privileged to foster a dozen children and produced two remarkable, almost-perfect beings. I feel I have lived—well. Part of me feels truly fulfilled, and the majority of me awaits my greatest blessings yet to come, as I watch my girls take on the world and marvel at their successes.

I have no memory of my parents being proud of me until the year of my diagnosis. Living on different sides of the country, we didn't spend much time together until my freefall from life that year. They rallied and came again and again to support me in every way possible. Looking back now, this is one of the greatest gifts of my life.

———————•———————•———————

"We do not know why your daughter has this cancer. I am sorry, but I cannot answer your question, although I wish I could," Dr. Guru said apologetically.

My mom seemed a bit less agitated by this nonanswer to her question. Maybe it was the validation of being involved and being able to exercise her right to ask questions. I know if I were ever, God forbid, to find myself in the mother seat at a hospital, there is no way I would sit quietly. No one would be able to keep me from asking questions and demanding answers and actions and solutions. I felt guilty about my frustration and impatience with taking time to field questions to which I knew there were no answers.

After emerging from Dr. Guru's office, my parents were escorted back to the waiting room, and I was led to a large medical chair to have more blood drawn and fill out more forms. I was given a sedative while I was signing away. A twenty-something woman in a lab coat approached me with a clipboard and asked if I would be willing to donate any parts of the tumor not needed for diagnosis and future testing to a research team from Harvard. The team was trying to determine why there was a sudden increase in this form of bad-luck cancer in women. I was happy to give any extra parts away to try to save anyone else from this nightmare.

I actually felt insulted when she then said apologetically that I would not be eligible for any royalties should a cure or treatment be found. Really? I wondered if anyone ever said "Well, never mind then. I don't want you to use any of those leftovers to try to save the thousands suffering after me. I would rather have it all tossed as medical waste if I'm not going to be paid." Does anyone truly believe a cancer cure should be about money? But of course it is, to some extent. Cancer has become big business for pharmaceutical companies, but I can't believe any patient wouldn't readily volunteer to have extra bits or pieces used in the pursuit of trying to help those who follow.

C'mon.

In filling out the reams of questionnaires given to me by all those smart Harvard interns, I did answer *yes* twice but came close to three times. My three risk factors identified among the hundreds of questions were: my mother smoked while pregnant with me and during my childhood, I had smoked cigarettes in my distant past, and I had undergone chronic stress during my marriage and the three years it took to get divorced. The stress had been constant. Most studies show stress in and of itself will not cause cancer, but the body may be less likely to fight off those oncogenes, giving them a chance to take hold and multiply. I in no way blame my divorce for my cancer. I do, however, feel it likely contributed.

There is a scene in the movie *Hairspray* where Edna and Tracey get all dolled up and dance and sing their way into a bar. At the bar are two fabulous-looking women sipping on martinis and smoking. The bar stools spin around, and the audience sees they are both pregnant. I can imagine my mother in that scene—sitting at a bar, being the most fabulous-looking woman there (although she would be having a gin and tonic instead of the martini, and it would be hard to tell she was pregnant). Of course now the scene is astonishing and disturbing, but back then it was sophisticated and chic. My mom was twenty-two when I was born in 1965 on the army base in Fuerth, Germany. Warning labels didn't come out on cigarettes in the United States until 1966, and President Nixon's "war on cancer" didn't begin until the end of 1971. It took a while before society caught up with the fact that smoking causes health issues.

The medical profession defines a nonsmoker as someone who has smoked fewer than one hundred cigarettes in her lifetime. I have to admit, although I consider myself a nonsmoker, I am on the fence here. Although I have never been a smoker the way I think about smokers, I did light up sporadically well over twenty-five years ago. Stephanie has a picture of me at about eighteen, and I'm sitting on the floor of her kitchen with a cigarette hanging from my mouth, flipping her off. Not my most flattering photo. She and I had the whole conversation, working out the math to see if I may have edged into the triple-digit realm with cigarettes. I ended up marking *no*, as I feel even though I am on the cusp that if I were to mark a yes, that would put me in the same pile of questionnaires as those who smoked two or three packs a day for decades.

So why me? Or for a better question, why the tens of thousands of other patients who are nonsmokers who will be diagnosed this year? According to the American Lung Association, lung cancer rates among women have more than doubled in the past thirty-five years. As a mother of two girls, this unexplained rise scares the bejeezus out of me.

We need to help figure this one out.

I changed into my now-familiar uniform of bluish, lightweight cotton adorned with the white accent ties and headed down the hall to have my lung punctured. The room was cluttered and seemed in harmony with the broom-closet office. It did not have the same operatic-music-swelling feel of substance and antiseptic analysis the CT room had held.

Three medical staff crowded in with me—Dr. Guru, a junior doctor, (likely a resident), and a nurse. Dr. Jr. placed me on the table on my left side for the procedure and went about putting in pads and bolsters to keep me still. I wasn't paying much attention, as I was checking out the machines and the monitors to determine how this was all going to work. Dr. Guru was in a back room (I had the sense he was moving boxes out of the way or sweeping up or trying to find a scalpel), but he was alert enough to come out and ask me to turn over and wrote a note with a Sharpie on my shoulder, indicating it was my *left* lung being punctured. So all the pillows and bolsters were rearranged as I flipped over and was restrapped down, my left arm held down over my head. I was given an intravenous sedative mix of midasolam and fentanyl, as well as some local anesthesia.

I felt the pinch of the needle being inserted, but it wasn't painful. The nurse suggested I not look, but I watched the monitor anyway as the hollow needle was moved to the mass and another needle was inserted through its hollow center to suction out part of the tumor.

Overall the biopsy wasn't so bad. I don't have a particularly high pain threshold, but I have had two babies, so in a relative sense, my bar may be higher than some.

Obviously there are some risks with a biopsy. The two most common risks are hemoptysis and pneumothorax, which occurs when the air and gas build up between your lung and chest wall, causing your lung to collapse. In the past ten years, about 20 percent of patients have experienced pneumothorax after a needle biopsy, which doesn't seem surprising to me, since the lung is being punctured, after all, so I'm not sure why they don't all deflate. But the body is remarkable and repairs itself pretty easily. If the lung does collapse, it's usually a relatively easy fix. If it's a slow leak, you will need to be monitored for about a week while your body takes care of it; a needle or chest tube will be put in to take care of the problem; or for bigger issues, an operation will sew you back up.

Hemoptysis is simply the coughing up of blood, which might happen if the lung tissues are irritated or had some minor damage during the biopsy. It's usually not a big deal and takes care of itself.

Neither of these things happened with me.

I didn't have any real discomfort with the biopsy, and I found the hardest part was lying face down for a few hours afterward. Try it— without moving. I was nervous to move, in case I bled into my lung or I thought it might deflate unless given the chance for the puncture wound to close up. I was able to rest for some of it, but I grew incredibly bored and restless. The nursing staff was attentive and would come by from time to time and check on me. They also brought a type of x-ray machine to take an image of my chest while I was lying there, to check that the hole was closing up okay and there were no issues with air filling the chest cavity or any bleeding problems. My parents were often in my periphery. I could make out their waists at the side of my gurney out of the corner of my eye. It was at about the time I really needed to go to the bathroom that I was finally released from my faceplant. You might consider going before the biopsy, as it is quite a while before you can get up again, and the bedpan option is not appealing. At least not to me.

After my quick pit stop, we headed to the imaging department, and I had one more chest x-ray to make absolutely certain I was good to go. I lost track of the number of x-rays I had over the course of treatment, but I know I kept thinking it seemed like quite a bit of radiation.

For that day, we were done. We were done until Sunday, when the big issue of metastasis would be addressed.

Biopsy Results:

FINAL DIAGNOSIS

A. LUNG FNA BIOPSY, LEFT UPPER LOBE:

SPECIMEN ADEQUACY:
Satisfactory for evaluation.

INTERPRETATION:
POSITIVE FOR MALIGNANT CELLS.

DIAGNOSIS:
Adenocarcinoma.

B. LUNG CORE BIOPSY, LUL:
Adenocarcinoma.

C. LUNG CELLBLOCK, LEFT UPPER LOBE:
Blood and rare atypical cells.

PET Scans

PET stands for *positron emission tomography* and got its birth in the 1950s at Mass General Hospital. Its fathers were neurosurgeon William Sweet and physicist Gordon Brownell. They developed the scan to help diagnose diseases of the brain, and the first images were two-dimensional and quite cloudy and indistinct. Not surprisingly, PET scans' use and efficacy have substantially improved in the past sixty years.

Basically what happens in a PET scan is a radioactive chemical goes into your body and is combined with a natural element (usually glucose, water, or ammonia). In my case, FDG (fluorodeoxyglucose) was the radiopharmaceutical used for my radiotracer. The glucose goes through the body and stops off at areas that use it—including cancer cells. As the glucose is broken down at these sites, positrons are made. When the images are done, the doctors can see all the areas of energy throughout the body created as the radiotracer is broken down and positrons are made. Where MRIs and CAT scans show us what the organs look like—their anatomy and structure—PET scans show us how well the organs are functioning and any chemical and physiological metabolic changes going on. These pathological changes are often present well before any of the structural changes show up on CAT scans or MRIs—a one-stop diagnostic system for total early detection of any and all cancer.

Pretty incredible.

Sunday marked one week since Dr. Howser told me of my mass, and that morning my father and I headed to the MGH imaging department in Chelsea to have my PET scans done. The building is a nondescript one-story brick building in what Maggie would call a slightly sketchy neighborhood. My dad brought along a good book and some magazines to keep content and got as comfortable as one can in a waiting-room chair as I filled out yet more forms and releases. I was then asked to change into the ever-lovin' hospital smock and ushered to a small, comfortable room, where I would be sequestered as I drank my chemical concoction and was given the FDG infusion while I awaited the scans. So there I was, taking part in nuclear medicine. I had a good book, and the room was fairly comfortable. I couldn't take the drink out or be in the waiting room, as I was becoming radioactive, which might be problematic for some. I was asked to remain quiet during this time and not to talk. I'm not sure what that was all about.

It takes about thirty to sixty minutes for the chemicals to make their way to where they need to go. I texted with my dad in the other room and fantasized about what I would eat for lunch—that's the other thing, nothing to eat or drink for four to six hours before the procedure.

After my percolation time was done, I was led into a room similar to the CAT-scan chamber with a big donut-shaped machine and a bed. This time I got earplugs, and my head was bolstered and buckled in for the scan, which took about thirty to forty-five minutes. I was given a panic button to push if I felt uncomfortable and was given the option of taking antianxiety medicine.

I once again put my arms over my head and slid into the donut. This machine is pretty loud and makes clanky noises (hence the earplugs), and it did take me to my limit of confinement. When the tech came in to help me out of the contraption, I had a moment of panic because my head felt stuffy and I could not hear well. It was solved right away when he pointed out that I still had the earplugs in.

A little embarrassing.

I tried again to get some sort of answer as to whether he noticed any unusual growths in my brain, but he too was mum.

And that was it. The most painful thing was the needle prick for hooking up the IV drip of FDG. I will say, on my way out there was a woman who had had an allergic reaction to something and was being wheeled past me on a gurney. It's very rare, and when it does happen, the patient is in a hospital setting, filled with capable people who are trained to handle the situation.

I was told to stay away from the very old, the very young, and small pets for twenty-four hours. I was also told my pee might glow in the dark for a day or so, but that didn't happen for me. I have to admit to being a little disappointed by that.

I went out and collected my dad, and we went out for a cheeseburger. Best meal ever. (And that comes from a quasi-vegetarian). I was starving. We then left the sketchy neighborhood and headed home.

Dr. Cusick called the next evening to say the PET scan showed no areas of concern other than the left upper lobe of my lungs. My second "floor item" had been handled; no metastasis to the brain. The biopsy reports were also back, and the tumor was malignant. As with 9/11, I think each of us will remember exactly where we were when we learned of our diagnosis. I had taken the phone to the den. My parents and daughters were in the kitchen, a fire was going, and I had to sit down, as my legs gave way. I could hear my girls prattling on about something and had to listen carefully for the positive things Dr. Cusick was saying—"Caught it early"; "Operation can remove it"; "May not even need chemotherapy"; "Good shot at beating this"; "Excellent medical care." I clung to those and made certain my overview of the call referenced all those positive remarks, so my parents and daughters would feel we were launching the fight from a good, solid footing.

And to try to convince myself of the same thing.

There is an identification system to cancer, set up to quickly ascertain a fairly complete diagnosis and to best determine treatment. The TNM staging system is often used and is based on three key pieces of information. The T refers to the main tumor and how big it is and whether or not it's grown into nearby sites. The N stands for nodes and looks at whether the cancer has made its way to nearby lymph nodes. The M covers metastasis to other organs in the body. These three pieces of information form your battle plan.

Cancer is further staged by subcategories of numbers and more letters. The American Cancer Society does a great job explaining the tiers on their website, Cancer.org. Basically issues escalate with the numbers 0 to 4. (The medical world uses roman numerals, so it's actually 0 to IV.)

My official diagnosis was adenocarcinoma, stage IIA NSCLC (T2bN0M0). This translates as stage 2 cancer (2 because it was only in one spot but the tumor was pretty big—5.2 x 5.3 x 4.0 cm or about 2 inches by 2 inches by 1.5 inches, for those of us not metrically inclined); the A since it had not spread. NSCLC stands for non-small-cell lung cancer, T is for tumor, 2b means the tumor was five to seven centimeters, N is for lymph nodes affected, 0 means none of mine were, M is for metastasis, and 0 means my cancer had not spread.

This, in lung cancer language, is about as good as it gets. This is the Hail Mary, hallelujah, praise be of lung cancer diagnoses. Of course, as Jeff Buckley sings in one of my favorite versions of the song, "It's a cold and it's a broken hallelujah."

REPORT—PET/CT OF CHEST CT scan of the chest WITH intravenous contrast in conjunction with PET scan.

This study was part of a combined PET-CT examination. Interpretation is in collaboration with other subspecialty Radiologists and Nuclear Medicine physicians. Please refer to all reports for a full description of findings pertaining to this PET-CT.

HISTORY: As given in the header.

COMPARISON: CT chest 2/19/2013.

FINDINGS:

Lungs: There is a lobulated mass measuring 5.1 x 3.7 cm in the left upper lobe best seen on image 61. There is a small cavity within the mass best seen on image 45. There is minimal surrounding interstitial thickening and groundglass opacity, reaching up to the pleura. There is a 4 mm nodule in the left upper lobe on image 55. There is minimal dependent atelectasis.

Pleura: There is no evidence of pleural effusion or pneumothorax.

Heart and mediastinum: There are stable small left hilar and suprahilar lymph nodes measuring up to 6 mm. There are stable scattered mediastinal lymph nodes measuring up to 7 mm, the largest lymph node is in the left paratracheal station on image 43. The cardiac chambers are normal in size. There is no pericardial effusion.

Bones and soft tissues: There are no suspicious lytic or blastic lesions.

IMPRESSION:
PET positive mass in the left upper lobe, concerning for lung cancer. Small left hilar and left mediastinal lymph nodes without associated FDG activity.

Indeterminate nodule in the left upper lobe.

Recommendation:
Advise follow up imaging in 3 months to assess change in small lung nodule.

REPORT PET-CT OF THE ABDOMEN AND PELVIS

COMPARISON: 2/19/2013

TECHNIQUE: CT of the abdomen and pelvis was performed as part of a combined PET-CT examination. Diagnostic CT was performed WITH intravenous contrast. CT and PET images were fused on a workstation and interpreted as part of a combined PET-CT readout.

FINDINGS:
LOWER THORAX: Please refer to report from concurrently performed chest CT.

HEPATOBILIARY: No focal hepatic lesions. No biliary ductal dilatation.
SPLEEN: No splenomegaly.
PANCREAS: No focal masses or ductal dilatation.

ADRENALS: No adrenal nodules.
KIDNEYS/URETERS: No hydronephrosis, stones, or solid mass lesions.
PELVIC ORGANS/BLADDER: Unremarkable.

PERITONEUM / RETROPERITONEUM: No free air or fluid.
LYMPH NODES: No lymphadenopathy.
VESSELS: Unremarkable.

GI TRACT: No distention or wall thickening.

BONES AND SOFT TISSUES: Unremarkable.

IMPRESSION:
No evidence of metastatic disease in the abdomen and pelvis.

REPORT PET/CT scan:

COMPARISON: None

TECHNIQUE:
15.79 mCi F-18 FDG was injected. Approximately 60 minutes later, tomographic images of the body from neck to proximal thigh were acquired. Images were reviewed in axial, coronal, and sagittal projections. The patient's blood glucose at the time of imaging was 109 mg/dl.

This study was performed as part of a combined PET/CT scan.
Diagnostic CT included the chest through proximal thighs. The neck PET was performed using low-dose CT attenuation correction without obtaining diagnostic CT images per clinical request. Separate subspecialty reports will be issued for the individual organ systems. Requesting physicians are referred to the reports from all components of the study.

FINDINGS:
There is intense FDG uptake throughout a soft tissue mass within the left upper pulmonary lobe.

A left upper lobe pulmonary nodule described on the CT report does not demonstrate significant FDG uptake, but are likely too small to be characterized by PET.

No FDG avid mediastinal or hilar adenopathy is noted.

Patterns of FDG uptake elsewhere in the body are within physiologic limits.

IMPRESSION:
Intense FDG uptake corresponding to left upper pulmonary lobe mass as described; no other FDG avid foci elsewhere in the body to suggest metastasis.

The first known cancer statistics were published in Verona, Italy, and the study tracked deaths from 1760 to 1839, during which time 994 women and 142 men died of cancer, or roughly 1 percent of the population. Today's death rate is around 25 percent, the increase attributed to detection, lifespan, and a surge in the use of tobacco.

Cancer used to be relatively rare, because it's primarily a disease of old age, and back in the day, cholera, typhus, tuberculosis, and dysentery were so prevalent, the vast majority of the population never reached their golden years. Life-expectancy tables are often hard to interpret, as child death rates have such an impact on averages. For example, in seventeenth-century England, life expectancy was about thirty-five—but this was mostly because two out of three kids died before age four. Seventeenth-century Puritans settling New England had it even worse—about 40 percent didn't reach adulthood, and Virginia's European settlers' life expectancy was under twenty-five. Many of our ancestors simply weren't living long enough to become a statistic of cancer, and in some instances, even if they did die of the disease, no one found out, since it often can't be seen by the naked eye, and most religions strictly forbade autopsies.

A medical report from 1912 found only 374 cases of lung cancer mentioned in international medical articles. The American Cancer Society estimates lung cancer cases in the United States for 2015 will be about 221,200 new cases (115,610 in men and 105,590 for women). They are estimating 158,040 deaths (86,380 in men and 71,660 in women). Lung cancer accounts for about 27 percent of all cancer deaths and is by far the leading killer among both men and women. Every five minutes a woman in the United States is told she has lung cancer. According to the American Cancer Society, each year more people die of lung cancer than of colon, melanoma, breast, liver, kidney, ovarian, and pancreatic cancer combined. *Combined.* Okay, let's not just gloss over this. *Lung cancer kills more than colon, melanoma, breast, liver, kidney, ovarian, and pancreatic cancer combined.*

The National Cancer Institute spends roughly $4.9 billion a year on cancer research. In 2012, the roughly $212 million granted to lung cancer research was less than a third of the funding for breast cancer, which received the biggest allocation of about $712 million. Those pink-ribbon gals are a force! They are to be admired for the amount of attention and funding breast cancer receives, and their hard work clearly shows. Breast cancer survival rates have climbed, and according to Cancer.net, "if the cancer is located only in the breast, the five-year relative survival rate of people with breast cancer is 99%." The American Cancer Society website states that breast cancer death rates decreased by 34 percent from 1990 to 2010 and puts the five-year survival rate of all patients at almost 90 percent. There is no question the amount of hard work and dedication given to the Pink Ribbon Tribe has paid off. But here's the thing: more of our mothers, daughters, aunts, sisters, nieces, and grandmothers die of lung cancer. A lot more. Not to mention all the men in our lives.

The lung cancer ribbon used to be clear before it was changed to white. I think a flashing neon emergency light with a blaring alarm would be more appropriate. At the very least, let's just make sure it stays visible.

We need to start paying more attention to this.

Four point nine billion is a lot of money. Here are a few statistics to put this figure in perspective: According to a 2014 report in *USA Today*, Americans spent $2.8 billion on Halloween candy, $117 billion on fast food, $7 billion for ATM fees, and $65.5 billion on lottery tickets. Here are some more fun facts from a 2012 article from mentalfloss.com: Americans spend $96 billion on beer, $11 billion on coffee, $65 billion on soft drinks, and $11 billion on bottled water. Wine sales reached $36.3 billion in sales in 2013, with $50 billion on alcohol. We Americans fork over about $250 billion to quench our thirst every year.

We also spend over $50 billion a year on our pets, or roughly ten times the amount the federal government spends on cancer research.

I don't know. I'm embarrassed to admit I spend more money on my pets, wine, and coffee than I donate to cancer research. And that's me. I feel pretty vested in a cure. There will be a cure someday; I know this. I am hopeful we can all think about donating toward research a bit more. Let's at least see if we can donate as much to cancer research as we spend on Halloween candy. Or Fido. Or Starbucks.

It would be a start.

Having a definite diagnosis is a good thing. It's not the yeses and nos in life that are hard to negotiate, but the maybes. "We're going to try to figure out what's wrong" is not a good slogan for cancer. I had a malignant tumor in my lung. That is a hard thing to have to deal with, but the problem is defined, and the solution is feasible and concrete. I am not the first to have lung cancer, and unfortunately neither will I be the last. I do have the benefit of the millions before me who each provided a small kernel of wisdom to the medical community; coupled with technological advances and an amazing medical team, I had significant fighting power. Armed now with a diagnosis, I could concentrate on the unfolding clarity of my game plan.

My next step: surgery.

The first thing to do before surgery is to find a surgeon, obviously.

First and foremost, there is no better time in history to combat cancer. There are smart, resolute, capable doctors who have dedicated their lives to researching and curing the very cancer I had. I was in the right place at the right time. Of course, it is a statistical fact a full 50 percent of doctors and surgeons graduate in the bottom half of their class. I needed to choose my medical team wisely.

My brother's work colleague had recently recovered from esophageal cancer and was actively involved in a national cancer organization. Mark called her and asked, "If you have lung cancer in Boston, who do you want as your surgeon?" Not surprisingly, she didn't know but knew someone who would. One of the doctors on the board of the cancer society with her was affiliated with the thoracic surgery department at Duke Medical Center. She said she would give him a call and get back. She did within the hour, with the answer that Dr. TG was not only the best in Boston but anywhere, and I should give him a call. I could use Dr. Duke's name if I would like.

I called Dr. TG's office at Brigham and Women's Hospital on Monday and was given an appointment for a consultation that Friday morning. I think it's a good idea to have at least two interviews; it gives you a chance to meet different personalities and to learn opinions and viable procedures.

On Tuesday my parents and I were back at MGH to meet with Dr. Amazing and the surgery team Dr. Cusick had recommended. Dr. Amazing was an excellent choice—quietly confident, personable, and accomplished. He let me know there would be an entire team devoted to me—an oncologist, a nutritionist, a social worker, a team of nurses, a behaviorist and therapist, and also clergy if I'd like; an all-encompassing service.

This surgeon showed me a poster of the human lungs. I was reminded there are five lobes—three on the right and two on the left. The left upper lobe makes up roughly 70 percent of that hemisphere. Dr. Amazing told me he would first make an incision at the base of my neck and remove and biopsy a couple of my lymph nodes, to ensure there wasn't any metastasis there; then he would focus on the tumor. He believed that to get a mass of that size out would necessitate cutting my ribs to remove my left upper lobe. This procedure would leave about a six-inch scar. The earliest he could do the surgery would be in two weeks. This was definitely the A-team, and I was confident they would do a good job. I did not, however, like the idea of waiting that long for surgery.

We left and were given directions to my pulmonary function test, to determine if I would be able to function with the diminished capacity resulting from removing 70 percent of my left lung. The pulmonary function test is almost fun. I breathed into a spirometer and got to watch the needles fluctuate as I tried to blow my lungs out through a hose. Then I sat in a Plexiglas chamber and blew into another tube and then walked up and down stairs with a monitor tracking exertion. I have always enjoyed doing well on tests and left with a report card of 125 percent—my lung function at the time. This translated to my lungs being capable of roughly 125 percent of average lung capacity. The tech told me without my left upper lung, I would be around 80 percent—about average. I would experience a difference of course and get winded more often, but I would not have any significant problems with basic activities.

I was so proud of my asthmatic, pneumonia-prone lungs with the big tumor. Superstars.

I was now ready for the next step—surgery. Interviewing Dr. TG on Friday was the last major item on my presurgery calendar. He happens to be the chief surgical officer of the Dana Farber/Brigham and Women's Cancer Center in Boston, and he teaches VATS (video-assisted thoracoscopic surgery) at Harvard Medical School. He is a thoracic god.

Friday morning, my parents and I headed to Brigham and Women's to meet and interview Dr. TG. We were ushered into an exam room with pictures of bisected lungs and torsos showing organs and charts of tumor staging. The door opened, and in walked Dr. TG.

Confident! Experienced! Brilliant! All these exuded from him and filled the room like a heady perfume. I bet my blood pressure lowered twenty points by being in the shadow of all that well-earned self-assuredness. Quite frankly, it helped that he looked like he belonged in central casting for *General Hospital*. And he was the perfect age too, late fifties, old enough to have gobs of experience but young enough to have a steady hand. That cancer had no chance.

After introductions, he said he'd had an opportunity to study my reports, and he too felt my best option would be to remove my left upper lung. He went over to the poster on the wall and outlined the portion of my lung he would remove.

"What is your surgical availability?" I asked.

"I could get you in in about ten days, two weeks. I would first do an operation to remove some of your lymph nodes, to establish the cancer has not spread. We would close you up and schedule the next operation to remove the mass in your lung. I can do it through VATS and only leave a few smaller scars. Most patients say VATS is easier to recover from. Those small scars won't even show up when you wear a bikini this summer," he said with a bit of a twinkle.

I was more than a little suspicious that he was toying with me; my body had not seen a bikini in decades. But it was distracting and nice to hear. I resolved to try to squeeze into a bikini to prove him right and imagined moving the straps to cover up those little scars.

"Oh. Well, that is certainly a consideration. By the way, what is VATS?" I was feeling I should be a wee bit more prepared but was not too proud to ask what was likely a stupid question.

"VATS stands for visually or video-assisted thoracoscopic surgery, and there is a lot of evidence suggesting it is easier to recover from and generally produces better overall results with fewer complications. Instead of making one large incision, we would make a few smaller ones, spread your ribs a little, and use a small camera to let us see what we need to know and exactly what to remove. You likely would not need to have chemotherapy, since there does not appear to be any metastasis. But if you do, you would likely get Carboplatin or Cisplatin along with Alimta. Most patients don't lose their hair with these drugs."

I was not at the point where I had wondered about losing my hair, but I had an inkling of being happy and relieved I likely wouldn't. My hair had not gotten onto my radar yet. It was not involved in any of my action steps of getting rid of cancer.

"So what questions should I be asking that I haven't yet, and what information should I know that I don't?"

"Hmmm." Dr. TG took a moment thinking it through. "You will be in the hospital for likely four to five days, and it will take about two years for you to fully recover. This is a major operation. You will lose some lung capacity and will likely not ever run a marathon."

I immediately was thinking about training for a marathon after surgery to be the contrarian and prove myself the most superior of patients. There was just that one thing about the surgery timing—I had to get the tumor out. I felt as though it was a time bomb about to metastasize and take over my body at any moment.

"That sounds pretty good. I interviewed a team at Mass General, and that surgeon suggested he could take a few of the lymph nodes and get them biopsied in about twenty minutes and if they appeared healthy go ahead and take the lobe out right then. Would that be possible?"

"I don't see why not." Dr. TG was completely fine with that. It made more sense to me. I'm not sure what the advantage was to do it the other way with two different surgeries. And it proved the benefit of having more than one interview. You can use knowledge from one to help shape your treatment to the way that works best for you.

"I have heard some great things about you. Dr. Duke said you were the absolute best to see in Boston. He couldn't say enough about you when he recommended you."

"Dr. Duke?" He seemed floored I would know of him. "I played golf with him a few weeks ago. Great guy."

"Mmm-hmmm." I, of course, had no idea who Dr. Duke was—just a name my brother was told over the phone from someone he worked with.

I didn't want to be misleading at all but wanted to warm him up a bit for my next question.

"I really have to get this tumor out of me. Is there any way to operate sooner?" I was welling up, thinking of how hard it would be to sit and wait for two weeks. The mass had already grown from 3.5 cm at the ER a week ago to over five. At that rate, I was scared it would break off and spread to other organs.

Dr. TG excused himself and returned ten minutes later. "I could get you in Monday morning at five if you are available."

"Perfect. See you then."

Surgery could finally be added to the calendar. There were a few more things to do before we could leave for the day—intake and blood and urine tests. Easy.

My parents and I headed back to see one of Dr. TG's nurses, to get my name on his operation list for Monday morning. She then sent us to the intake nurse to input my full medical history and review the information the hospital had on file. Preadmission testing is mandatory within a week of undergoing general anesthesia.

My intake nurse told me I "had the bloodwork and vitals of a twenty-year-old," that the only thing wrong with me was lung cancer. Now I never tire of telling my kids that. Although, let's face it, I realize she was sugar-coating it a bit (okay, a lot), it gave me some added confidence, and I loved the visual of my decidedly middle-aged self being compared to a twenty-year-old me.

She spent more than an hour going over every single medical issue I had ever had, all my sicknesses and symptoms and statistics. By the time she was done, she knew every medical matter I had experienced since birth. No scrape was too small to be considered and dutifully noted. Her efforts were painstaking. A nurse came in during the interview to take blood and get my blood pressure, which was still high. The nurse chatted away about how I was going to be fine and what to expect during my hospital stay.

"Your bloodwork is great!" she gushed, and I felt like a champion. "You know, twenty years ago the treatment would have been to go home and get your affairs in order—but not now. You're going to beat this." She said it with such conviction I believed her.

"Thank you." I'm not sure if nurses and doctors realize how much their words influence their patients, particularly the ones who are scared of death. This woman had found her calling, and we are all the better that she sits in that surgery gateway chair.

She told me many patients are out of it the night of the operation and wake up disoriented and in discomfort (medical jargon meaning pain). She said it can be helpful to have a familiar face to focus on, and she recommended someone stay with me that first night.

She wrapped up my medical record and sent me out to go pee in a cup for the last bit of information they could possibly glean from my body before surgery Monday.

I had had both the tests to confirm and narrow the diagnosis, along with the tests to determine what type of treatment I would need intermingled. MRIs and x-rays and a bazillion blood tests were done, and being at a first-rate hospital, these results were shared by computer and could be seen almost immediately by every department, and the patient herself, through the partner's website. My surgery was Monday, March 4, 2013—two weeks and a day from my ER trip. I have corresponded and spoken with many people who waited weeks for test results, *months* for surgery. I have no idea how they endure it.

Tips for Getting Ready for Your Operation

1) *Find your own Dr. Cusick and Dr. TG*—doctors you have utter, absolute faith in. Again, I am fortunate to be in the Boston area and have access to such great teams and resources. I would highly recommend finding a strong medical advocate like Dr. Cusick to fast-track tests so the tumor is removed as quickly as reasonably possible, if that is what you want. You are the driver here; these are your decisions. Be unreasonable and firm if you want your timeline to go faster. Some may be understandably a bit nervous about surgery and may want to psych themselves up for it, get used to the idea, learn more, and not rush. Whatever is best for you, find that doctor, that surgeon, that oncologist, that team, that will help you reach your goal.

Decide to be the best patient ever. *Commit* to the process of getting better. *Resolve* to do the absolute best you can.

2) *Try to have all your medical appointments and procedures at one facility or at linked facilities.* This makes it easier for information to be disseminated and shared by your medical team immediately. See if you can also gain access to your results via a patient gateway. If you decide to do chemo at a different hospital closer to home, make certain they have a copy of all your records, so if you end up with a bad reaction or side effect, they will have your records in their system.

3) *Get a second opinion.* If there is not another doctor or hospital in your area, the National Cancer Institute has designated comprehensive cancer centers all over. Call them and overnight a copy of your results and your slides. Include your pathology reports and any and all information retrieved from your body. Ask them to conduct an outside review of your diagnosis and treatment plan; insurance should cover this.

4) *Ask for small blood sample needles.* I am not a big fan of needles and had to have a bazillion blood tests. I asked for the little kids' or butterfly

needles, and the nurse would usually switch when I asked. Apparently they are more expensive, so they are generally not used on adults unless specifically requested. So if you have a thing about needles, ask away.

5) *Plan a vacation.* Have something fun to look forward to in six months or so. Planning it will be fun, and going will be a great reward for all the hard work you are about to undertake. Choose somewhere spectacular.

6) *Enlist some of the kids' (and your) favorite adults to take your kids out on a regular basis.* This will give them the opportunity to unload any questions or concerns and allow you another way to check in on how they are doing. My kids didn't want me to be worried about their worrying. I reached out to the moms of their good friends to ask if they could be included more often in any social activities. I also lined up therapists trained to help get kids through situations like ours. My cancer was sandwiched between my divorce and their father's death, so they had quite a bit of trauma and grief to contend with.

7) *Go to the dentist.* This is a strange one. There are all sorts of side effects with chemotherapy, and believe it or not, this might be a good time to get your teeth checked and cleaned before your gums get super sensitive.

8) *Go to the eye doctor.* If you wear contacts, you may want to splurge on some new glasses, as chemotherapy will likely leave your eyes dry, and wearing contacts may be uncomfortable.

9) *Think about freezing your eggs or sperm.* I have very little knowledge about this, but I do know chemotherapy and radiation are tough on the reproductive organs. If a child or children are in your future plans, you may want to get some advice about putting aside some eggs or sperm for future options.

10) *Investigate grocery delivery services.* We have a couple of grocery stores in the area that offer to shop and deliver; you simply go online and order

what you want. There is a delivery charge, but it may be well worth it the first couple of weeks after surgery.

11) *Take a picture of the area that is going to be operated on.* It's sort of a memento of what it has looked like your whole life up to surgery. I did glance in the mirror at my side and back without scars the night before. I did not take any pictures but had a moment of taking in the "beforeness" of my unmarred skin.

12) *Consider donating blood.* Autologous donations are when you donate your own blood, in the event you need a transfusion during surgery. You must get your doctor's approval, and it has to be done at least seventy-two hours prior to the operation. The obvious benefits are that you will know it is a good match and it is safe.

Tips for the Team

1) *Offer to go to appointments.* Many of the appointments require someone else to drive the patient home, and providing good, positive, distracting company is a great gift to give. Pack some healthy snacks and a water bottle or two. Bring along books, magazines, or an iPod. Take a variety of items to keep you busy; these are often all-day events.

2) *Provide referrals.* If you know of highly competent doctors, surgeons, or oncologists, let the patient know about them. If you know of someone who has been diagnosed with the same type of cancer and had great results, ask her if she would mind sharing the names of some people she feels would do a great job.

3) *Send notes or cards.* This is a busy time for a cancer patient; she may be hard to reach, as she may be lying knee deep in a PET scanner or MRI machine. Coming home to a funny card or a little note letting her know people are thinking of her and are there for support is reassuring. Or e-mail a link to a funny video or joke, something that will bring a smile or chuckle.

4) *Listen and validate.* This sounds simple but is astonishingly hard to do. Just listen. Let the patient get everything out, and listen. Listen and validate the concerns. Do not fall into the temptation to sugar-coat the situation or talk about your own experiences. Just listen.

5) *Offer to do stuff with the kids.* If she has school-aged children, she is likely struggling to keep up with the crushing amount of time and travel associated with after-school activities. It is extraordinarily helpful to have some of this drive time taken off the schedule. Offer to take the kids to ice cream or the movies or out to pizza. Chances are pretty good it may be stressful at home, no matter how hard everyone is trying to maintain a sense of normalcy. Try to help distract them and give them some fun things to look forward to.

6) *Give support to the significant other.* This is a difficult time for all involved, and attention should be given to the ones trying to keep it all together for the patient. A quick check in or lending an ear or a shoulder is important.

7) *Don't tell her to be positive*—or that she has a "good" type of cancer or God's will will see her through or that you know how she feels. These platitudes are generally not helpful.

8) *Gift basket ideas*—Going through cancer treatment is a long and expensive process. Financial support may be greatly appreciated and can vary depending on the circumstances. A basket might include more expensive essentials such as pet food, detergents, baby food, and cleaning products. Or put together gift certificates for utilities, a gas card, and grocery gift cards. A group gift may be able to cover a mortgage payment or send cash. There are few out there who don't need a little help from time to time.

9) *When you give her a hug, don't be the first to let go.*

The Operation

Courage is being scared to death but saddling up anyway.
—John Wayne

Ain't no try, ain't nothing to it but to do it.
—unknown

I like to remember how Cancer became a constellation. Hercules, the most kickass of all gods, was in a legendary battle with the Hydra. Hera (still annoyed her ever-cheating husband, Zeus, had begot Hercules with another woman) sent a giant crab to try to distract Hercules so the Hydra could finish him off. Well, Hercules was not falling for that and simply stomped on the giant monster's head so hard the crabmeat flew to the heavens, and we still see it up there today.

Now is the time for our own kickass crab stomping.

In the late 1800s Frederick Law Olmsted designed a park system in the Boston area called the Emerald Necklace. It's not much of a necklace really, more of a fishhook in shape, beginning at the Public Garden and hooking around to the baited barb of Franklin Park. The necklace stretches out seven miles and covers twelve hundred acres. The Riverway is a thirty-four-acre esplanade that follows the path of the Muddy River about a third of the way along the hook. Right across its banks sits a medical metropolis that includes the Brigham and Women's Hospital as well as the Dana Farber Hospital.

Back in the 1700s and early 1800s, well before any insurance companies, many of the houses in the Boston area were built of wood. The major source of light and heat was fire, and this created a need to help families whose homes burnt to the ground, so the Massachusetts Charitable Fire Society was established. Around 1825 Boston passed an ordinance requiring all new homes be built of brick. This freed up quite a bit of the Fire Society's funds, and $5,000 of their surplus went to start up a hospital where poor women could go to give birth. (Women with means gave birth at home, attended to by a personal physician and midwife.)

The September 29, 1832, *Christian Register* heralded the opening of the Boston Lying in Hospital. The article said, "No patient will be recommended for admission unless a married woman or one recently widowed, and known to be of good moral character." Despite these safeguards, a 1946 article in *Men and Books, Highlights in the History of the Boston Lying in Hospital* by Dr. Frederick C. Irving reports in the earlier days of the hospital, half the patients were "unmarried and either ignorant immigrant girls, or trollops, trulls, and tarts. For the first 5 years 52% were unmarried, in the last 5 years only 2%. Since birth control is illegal in Massachusetts a simple arithmetical calculation will convince you that Boston women of the present day are twenty six times more moral than were their great-grand-mothers."

Gracious.

After his father passed away, a teenaged Peter Brigham left Vermont and traveled to Boston to seek his fame and fortune. He ended up an example of the American dream—owning real estate and restaurants and becoming a founding member of the Fitchburg Railroad. He died in Boston in 1877, leaving no children and $1.3 million to build a hospital for the poor. The Peter Bent Brigham Hospital opened its doors in 1913. Peter's nephew, Robert, maybe not surprisingly, also made his fortune in real estate and restaurants. Following in his uncle's footsteps, the Robert Breck Brigham Hospital opened April 1, 1914.

The Peter Bent Brigham Hospital, the Robert Breck Brigham Hospital, and the Boston Lying in Hospital all merged to form Brigham and Women's Hospital in 1980. The Brigham and Women's website sums up its accomplishments pretty succinctly:

> Boston's Brigham and Women's Hospital (BWH) is an international leader in virtually every area of medicine and has been the site of pioneering breakthroughs that have improved lives around the world. A major teaching hospital of Harvard Medical School, BWH has a legacy of excellence that continues to grow year after year. With two outstanding hospitals and over 150 outpatient practices with over 1,200 physicians, we serve patients from New England, throughout the United States, and from 120 countries around the world.

The first ever lobectomy (not to be confused with lobotomy) was performed by the thoracic surgery pioneer Dr. Hugh Morriston Davies in London in 1912. Dr. Davies, the first to diagnose lung cancer by using an x-ray, successfully removed the tumor, but his patient died eight days later because the chest cavity was not drained properly. Surgical techniques have been continually perfected over the past century, and the cutting-edge (pun intended) surgery today is VATS. Video-assisted thoracoscopic surgery uses specialized instruments the surgeon inserts through three or four small incisions in the chest cavity. One of these instruments is a thoracoscope, which looks a little like a power-washer attachment. The first twenty or so centimeters are rigid, and the last five centimeters look like a small hose. There is a camera on the end of the rigid part that feeds images from inside the chest cavity to a TV monitor. Depending on what needs to be done, other surgical instruments can be manipulated through other small incisions.

I ended up with four small scars. Well, five if you count (and I guess we should) the inch-long scar at the base of my neck where the lymph nodes were removed to be biopsied. The other scars range from about an inch to around two inches and are on my side and under my arm. Dr. TG was right—if I were ever inclined to wear a bikini, they would not show.

Dr. TG removed the left upper lobe of my lung on the morning of March 4, 2013. My dad and I were up at four o'clock for the ride into Brigham and

Women's Hospital. Maggie was up to pack us a snack and to say good-bye. I woke my mom on the way out to say goodbye, and kissed Jane and told her I would be home in a few days.

Arriving at the hospital that early was a gift, because as hard as it is to go through surgery and chemotherapy, it is infinitely harder to find a parking space in the Boston area during working hours. The Brigham and Women's Hospital helps ease the issue with a valet service, which feels decadent when available. Even the valets have to close up shop from time to time, as parking becomes impossible.

I was processed along with about fifty other patients in the lower level of the hospital. My dad and I checked in, and the opaque plastic bracelet with my name and ID number on it was attached to my right wrist. The waiting room appeared more like one at an airport than a hospital, as nearly all of us had packed an overnight bag. Some still wore pajamas, and most were accompanied by one or two supporters. It was quiet; we spoke in whispers as though it were a library or church. I guess it was the solemnity of the occasion, and I could not help but wonder what everyone was in for. Obvious ailments disclosed by splints and crutches and slings were evident; others, like mine, were impossible to determine.

Most of my fellow travelers ranged in age from newly minted card-carrying members of AARP to those having spent years taking advantage of Medicaid.

Every so often I would catch someone's eye, and we would give a solemn smile and nod of camaraderie. After a brief wait, an attendant started calling names out in groups of five or so. Mine came up in the third roll call, and we were escorted into an office along a hallway.

"Good morning," said the woman behind the desk pleasantly. The small office was sterile, with little besides a desk, computer, printer, and a stack of files.

"Good morning." I gave a tired smile.

She checked my wrist tag and the file she had on her desk and input the information into her computer. A screen popped up, and she verified all my information. She then asked me if I would sign a health proxy.

"I have one with my legal papers and have signed a few these past couple of days."

"Would you mind signing another for our files?"

"No problem." I didn't mind but felt it somewhat disturbing to have to sign over and over again who would be responsible for pulling my plug and figuring out my funeral arrangements. I didn't have any doubt my surgery would be successful, but it made me wonder if the hospital had my level of confidence. I was not nervous in the least. I was actually a little eager for surgery. I wanted the tumor out so much I had not contemplated any risks or complications or pain. I usually want to read books, talk with others about their experience, research Internet sites (and yes, you can watch a video of a lung being removed online), and be as fully briefed as possible. This time, though, I just wanted to go in and get it over with. I didn't feel I had an option, so it wouldn't matter what I learned. I was going to do it anyway and then move on to the next step in my battle plan.

After my paperwork had been sufficiently checked and rechecked, we were escorted further down the hall and entered an arena of activity centered around a nurses' station. There was a frenzy of activity as people were handing over their overnight bags and clothing and getting into the blue johnnies distinguishing them as patients.

My dad and I were escorted to a cubicle set to one side, and I was handed my own oh-so-chic johnny. My father excused himself while I changed and lay down on a gurney. He returned with a young doctor who was charged with getting the stents and various tubes and wires and machines hooked up to me. The doctor was apologetic, as he had some difficulty with getting the needle to hit a vein and had to take a few stabs at it. Which means, of course, he had to take a few stabs at my arm. My dad gave me the questioning "What the heck?" look, and I gave him the "Whatcha gonna do?" look in response.

I was eventually all wired and taped up, and the young doctor double-checked the machines to make sure everything was as it should be. Dr. TG walked in wearing blue scrubs and a surgical hat with a mask hanging down around his neck. He shook my dad's hand and gave my shoulder a squeeze, as he quickly reviewed the younger doctor's handiwork.

"Ready?" he asked, looking me in the eye.

"Ready as I'll ever be."

"Okay, let's do this."

They wheeled me into the operating room, my dad trailing behind. I remember seeing a room smaller than I had expected and the ultra-bright overhead lights. Then nothing. I guess they started the anesthesia drip sometime in there, but I was waiting to do the countdown backward from one hundred by sevens like you see in the movies.

Next thing I knew, someone was moaning.

Turns out it was me. I woke myself up with my groans. I didn't immediately realize where the noise was coming from and glanced around a bit before understanding that the sound was my body commenting on the fact it felt like it had been run over by a steamroller. I felt wrapped in the heavy, bruising cocoon of exhaustion. I looked around and discovered I had awoken in a small, curtained-off cubicle in a hallway somewhere, and a nurse immediately was by my side, checking my stats on the machine. She gave me a warm smile and squeezed my arm. "I am going to go get your parents. They are waiting for you."

There's something in the essence of a hospital that tells of its surroundings—like being at the beach or a Laundromat or snuggling a newborn baby—a hospital has its own signature effluence. There is an echo in the hum of machines, fluorescent lights, and murmured voices; the smell of diluted bleach and stress and too many patients is carried in the still air, where a heaviness and staleness pervades the pores and leaves a film of anxiety.

I nodded to the nurse and closed my eyes, opening them again when I sensed my parents had arrived. I managed to give them a thumbs-up sign and a little smile before drifting off.

When I awoke again, I was in my recovery room, a spacious room on the fifth-floor wing reserved for thoracic-surgery patients. The room was one of six or seven fanning a nurses' station and designed to accommodate two patients, but no other bed was in my room. My parents were sitting in chairs next to me, and after a quick check-in to make sure I was okay, they headed home to rest and relax and enjoy a well-earned bottle of wine.

I had looked at my surgery through a keyhole, not looking at the whole picture but rather as a frieze—bright lights, a white room, and myself lying on an operating table with the legs and back of Dr. TG obscuring the view. I hadn't thought about being on oxygen or having a catheter when I woke up. This may seem like an "of course," but I hadn't considered it, and I am embarrassed to admit I thought I should have tried to fit in a bikini wax. I blame the drugs for this absurd nod to vanity. I didn't realize I would have a tube coming out of my side, filling a container with blood and fluids draining from my chest cavity. This doesn't sound very pleasant, because it's not. I learned that during lung surgery, the chest cavity fills with fluid and blood, which makes sense, since your lung is deflated and, in my case at least, a good chunk taken out. The tubes are connected to a machine that has a little suction to help the drainage process, and the markings on the container track the amount that's collected. Once the liquids stop flowing, they disconnect it. The machine also helps the lung refill with air—which is a good thing.

In recovery I wore nifty boot-socks called compression boots that give a little squeeze on the lower legs to keep the blood circulating and help prevent venous thromboembolism (VTE) which can lead to blood clots—a common complication with surgeries. My nurse told me astronauts wear them too.

Pretty much everything my body needed to do was outsourced to some type of machine.

Anyone who has ever been in a hospital knows sleeping for any length of time is impossible. There are a multitude of interruptions and noises and harassments that wake you. I was given a cord with a joystick on it that when pressed would open up the valve for the pain medication. I used it liberally. I was told perhaps a bit too liberally and it was set up on a timer so I could only access the medication periodically. I can't remember what the interval was now, but it did slow down my intake.

I was so exhausted that first day of recovery, I did little else than sleep whenever possible. Dr. TG stopped in on his rounds and told me the six-hour surgery had gone well. There was no lymph node involvement, and my margins were clear. Someone Up There was still on the job. The cancer cells were well defined, meaning the malignant cells were close to what they should have been, a little haywire, but not a complete failure of attempting the perfect replication; like using a wrong paint in a color by numbers.

I texted my girls several times throughout the day, as I was too tired to have a conversation, and my voice sounded weird and scratchy from the tube that had been placed down my throat throughout the operation. My lung had been deflated during surgery, and I was connected to a ventilator that breathed for me while Dr. TG did his job.

Another surprise was how much my left arm and shoulder bothered me. In order to have a clear view of my chest cavity, my arm had been strapped down over my head. Quite a few people I chatted with online following this procedure had the same experience. It was a bit painful—a sort of stiff, bruising feeling that lasted a few days. From what I have read, it is a common side effect.

I did manage to get vertical and shuffle down to get an x-ray that first day of recovery. I wasn't able to lift my left arm at all, but the technicians were able to get what they needed anyway. I was glad to have a sweater that buttoned down the front to wear on my sojourn and a pair of warm, nonslip socks. I will add a list of some other suggestions to pack for the hospital at the end of this chapter.

By Wednesday morning I felt it was time to get back to my game plan. Tuesday had been spent pretty much bedridden, and I was now ready to get back into the swing of functioning on my own. The nurses removed my oxygen nose plugs, took out my catheter, and escorted me on a walk around the floor. The distance was advertised on a paper taped to the wall, saying one circuit equaled an eighth of a mile. My going was slow, and one fellow lapped me as I shambled slowly around.

"Show-off," I said to him with a smile.

He was in his sixties and wheeled an oxygen tank. The scars on his chest belied his ongoing battle with heart and lung disease.

"Hey, you've got to do this thing. No one's going to do it for you. You've got to do the best you can and work at it every single day." Excellent advice. And with a smile, he rounded the corner with what, for me, was remarkable alacrity and speed.

I continued my slow shuffle.

I felt a lot of aloneness with my cancer. It's quite a realization to know how solitary one is and how isolated one can feel throughout the process. No one can do this for you. No one can take some of your struggle and say, "I'll deal with this part so you don't have so much." Have you ever seen the movie *Cool Hand Luke*? I'm not sure why I'm thinking about it. It's a 1967 movie with Paul Newman, who plays a prisoner, Luke, in a Florida prison camp. He is super cool and irreverent and inspiring to the other prisoners. He tries to escape several times, and after each attempt, he is caught and brought back and tortured by the super-mean prison guards. After one escape attempt, Luke is forced to eat a huge bowl of rice. I can't remember why, although I do remember for whatever reason it would be impossible for him to eat it all, and the guards were threatening all sorts of punishment if he didn't. So the other prisoners all take a spoonful on their way by as he sits with his heaping bowl at the cafeteria table. That would be helpful here, if everyone could just take a little spoonful of struggle on their way by.

I did another lap and then slept for a bit before the nurse escort, with a gentle hand under my elbow, walked with me to get another set of x-rays. I had three rounds of x-rays on Wednesday, at nine in the morning, noon, and three in the afternoon; I shuffled around one extra lap at noon and two extra laps at three.

By Thursday the IV was gone, and I was dressed and spending more of the day out of bed. I ordered healthy food, and I have to say the vegetable soup was much better than I had expected. I sat in the chair in my room to eat and walked several times, trying to add on laps and go a little faster. The nurse no longer walked with me. I just shuffled along, carting my blood and fluid pack on wheels. I had one follow-up x-ray right after breakfast around eight thirty. Things were healing fine.

Stephanie was my only company. She visited me late Thursday afternoon, and I felt bad that I couldn't stay awake for long. I had told friends not to come in; I was just too tired, and the trip in with parking and the winter weather would make me want to visit longer than I should, to make it worth the trip. Stephanie wouldn't listen. She brought me magazines and pajamas and warm, fuzzy, nonslip socks—great gift ideas for someone in the hospital for a few days. Her flowers were confiscated, since they are not allowed in the thoracic wing. The hospital doesn't want to take the chance there would be an allergic reaction to compromise an already risky lung condition.

I FaceTimed my girls on Thursday after my brief nap following Stephanie's visit. Jane and Maggie were lying together on a big beanbag in our family room with the computer on Jane's lap.

"Hey, baby! What's up?" I was sitting upright and fully dressed and sounding as energetic and upbeat as possible.

"Hey, Mom! Not much. I had to go to school today, and it was boring."

"Hi, Mom," said Maggie from the background. She was studying me carefully, and I could see tears starting to form. She had been scared.

"Hey, baby. How are you, honey?"

"Okay."

"We're having macaroni and cheese for dinner tonight—the kind Nani makes that's so good," Jane piped up. She was busy watching her own picture on the bottom of the screen, making faces at herself.

Maggie wiped away tears and gave me a heartfelt smile. I don't think she trusted the texts; I don't think she knew yet I would be okay. This was her first proof.

"Want to see my room?" I asked.

"Sure."

I held up my phone and moved it slowly around in a circle, letting them see the whole room.

"You get your own TV in your room?" Jane squealed.

"Yep. Pretty fancy, huh? Like a hotel. I love you!" I said to them both, feeling at the limit of my strength. "Enjoy that mac and cheese. I'll be home soon. Save me some. I love you!"

"Okay, Mom. See you soon! Love you!" And with that and a few air kisses, I fell back to sleep.

Friday the weather report called for a big storm to hit Boston. A nurse arrived with a few medical students to take out my chest tube. I was a little nervous, as it seemed like sort of an important thing to do, and maybe a full-on doctor should have been in charge.

"These are some students who would like to be present—is that okay with you?" she asked.

"Sure, of course."

"This tube is draining the fluids from the chest cavity, and this shows us how much has been collected." She indicated the almost-full clear container with markers showing levels of output. Not to be gross, but the output looked a little like bloody saliva, and there seemed like quite a bit of it—although I have no reference point.

"There is a stitch left in her side that needs to be tightened once the tube is out." The three medical students craned their necks to catch a glimpse of the black nylon slipstitch near the incision site.

"The patient should hum while the tube is being removed. This will ensure there is no intake of breath." She glanced at me, and I started humming. She positioned herself to pull out the tube and then hesitated and suggested we start again. So I hummed away, and she pulled the tube out, tugged the stitch tight, and put a bandage over the incision. And that was it.

There were two things the nurses said they were waiting for to get me discharged. One was to make sure I could walk up and down a flight of stairs. This did not happen before I was let go, and I don't know why. It was not a big deal, though. The second big thing was to have a bowel movement. Constipation is a common issue with surgery and pain medication. I had not had one since Sunday. It was now Friday, and they started pulling out the heavy-duty laxatives to get my system moving—but nothing budged. They then pulled out the *super*-heavy-duty laxatives. Still nothing budged. I had been told several times I would not be let go until my plumbing had been fully tested; then I was told I would be discharged anyway.

I had yet another set of x-rays, to check that there weren't any issues created by taking out the drainage tube. The nurse entered my room and said I would need to stay another day or so, as there was an air pocket showing up in the lining of my lung that was a concern. She was going to have Dr. TG look at it right away. My parents were already on their way in to get me, and the weather was just beginning to turn to a full winter storm. I called them to let them know there might be a change of plans. They decided to come in anyway and hoped I would be freed about the time they arrived. I was dressed and packed and decided to walk around a bit while waiting. I ran into Dr. TG in the hallway, and he said he was not worried at all about the air pocket, so I should head on home. He would see me on Tuesday for a follow-up appointment.

My parents were in the waiting room, and I gave them the good news and then shuffled quickly back to my room to gather my bags and head home.

Let's face it—getting to go home is a big part of what life is all about.

Things to Pack for a Hospital Stay:

Take in all your medical forms, insurance card, doctors' numbers, and your family contact information, prescription drugs, allergy information, and a copy of your health proxy or living will.

1) *Bring your own pillow and light blanket.* It is nice to have something from home, and isn't your own pillow the best? Put it in a colorful pillowcase so you don't forget it when you go home.

2) *Books and magazines.* Magazines are best to flip through and not have to concentrate too much on. Or bring a poolside book that is fast paced and does not need too much thought. Kindles are good too; never run out of selections.

3) *Check to see about bringing in your cell phone.* I was able to bring mine, and it had games and music to keep me entertained. It was also a great way to stay in touch via texting. Don't forget to pack your charger.

4) *A laptop or tablet,* especially if you need and feel up to checking in with work. Take along the chargers.

5) *Headphones,* so you can listen to music or movies from your phone or computer without disturbing others.

6) *Pack your glasses* if you wear them.

7) *Toiletries*—toothbrush, toothpaste, brush/comb, small container of shampoo and conditioner. Add Chap Stick and some hand lotion.

8) *Take along shirts, sweaters, or sweatshirts that button or zip down the front.* You do not want to be tugging things over your head, and you will need the opening for your tubes and various medical devices.

9) *Pack nonstick slippers or socks.*

10) *Earplugs and an eye mask.* These might help you sleep a little better.

11) *Pack your journal* to keep track of medications, questions and answers, and symptoms you may be having.

12) *Bring your prescriptions and supplements.* Make certain your medical team knows what you are taking, to ensure they do not interfere at all with other medications you will be put on.

13) *Pack knitting, crochet projects, crossword puzzles, thank-you cards,* or other things to keep you busy.

14) *Many people like to bring in small framed pictures* to put on the nightstand to make it a little homier.

15) *Include comfy pajamas and sweatpants.* The hospital gown gets old quickly. Get into some of your own comfortable clothes as soon as you can.

16) *Get extra support and coverage.* If you feel you need more help than you were able to line up, contact the American Cancer Society. They have access to volunteers and social workers to help you. Do not go home without someone there to assist you. Check out the resources at the end of this book.

Other Tips for the Operation:

1) *Be comfortable with the amount of information you have* about the operation. Everyone wants a different level of assurance or knowledge about the various procedures and risks involved. Whatever level you need, make sure you are there when you go in.

2) *Try to schedule the operation for a morning if possible.* You will likely have to fast, which can be tough, and it may also be hard to sit around and wait during the day before going in.

3) *Stock a pile of pillows in the car to prop up around you on the way home.* You will be sore around your operation site, which may be impacted by your seat belt.

4) *When you are discharged, you will be told to not lift anything heavier than five pounds.* This (thank goodness) includes grocery bags, laundry detergent, garbage bins, and dog food. You may also (and I got this in writing) be told to stay away from household cleaning products for a while. So revel in your doctor-ordered relaxation, and be content to be untroubled by all household obligations.

5) *Retain a copy of any and all of your medical reports.* Hospitals will put these on a disc for you. Your medical reports are legally yours, and you may want easy access to them for future appointments, to get second opinions, or should you ever move.

6) *Ask what will be done with your tumor.* This seems a bit macabre, but medical science is moving very quickly, and more and more target treatments are being developed. If your particular type of cancer cell is not yet eligible for one of these smart-bomb type treatments, it may be in the future, and you want to make certain your tumor cells are available to test. I don't know where all these leftovers are kept—and frankly, I do not particularly want to think about it—I just know my tumor is being stored. In the unlikelihood of a recurrence, we will have

an ample sample to test, to see if the cells are a fit for any new drug treatment that has come along.

7) *Invest in a good thermometer and a pill-reminder case.* You will want to keep close tabs on your temperature to make sure your body is not fighting off more than you already know. I took my temperature every morning and every night and recorded it. Anything over 100.5 needs to be reported right away to your medical team.

You will be on prescriptions for the foreseeable future. If you are headed to chemo and the accompanying brain fog, do yourself a favor and get one of those pill cases with the days on it. A good bet would be to get one with morning and evening slots. You will likely have to take some medications more than once a day. Jane made me one from a bead dispenser and glued on rhinestones. I use it every day, and it always makes me smile.

8) *Stock up on camisoles and comfortable undershirts.* After surgery to your chest area, you are going to be sore, putting it mildly. Wearing a bra is not going to do you any favors. Get some soft cotton or silk undershirts or camis. Use a strategically tied scarf if you feel you need more coverage.

Tips for the Team

1) *Provide a ride to and from the hospital.* Offer to stay in the hospital with her that first night after the operation.

2) *Check with the hospital to see what is acceptable to send in.* Flowers may not be permitted, but maybe a fruit basket or other food items might be welcome. A nice idea is to send something to the nurses' station as a thank-you for taking care of the patients.

3) *After the operation, text or e-mail to see if she is up for company.* Take in some magazines or snacks or just yourself for good company and support. Be careful not to stay too long; she will likely be tired, and the visit should be kept short. Of course, do not visit if you are sick or even feel you might be coming down with something.

4) *Take care of the kids during the hospital stay.* Offer to drive to after-school activities or take the kids to dinner or for an overnight. Keep them busy.

5) *Keep an eye on her partner or spouse.* This is a stressful time for all those close to the patient. Significant others should reach out for extra support from family, friends, or therapists.

6) *Pets may need attention too.* If you are up for it, offer to take the dog or cat or fish or gerbil or whatever combination she might have going on for the duration. This can be a huge help.

7) *Line up the meal wagon*, and have someone who will check in to help with errands for the next couple of weeks. It may be awhile before the patient can drive, because she will be on pain medication.

8) *See if any household things need to be addressed*—mowing, weeding, watering, snow shoveling, trash pickup, babysitting, laundry, or grocery shopping. Look into the patio plants or window boxes. If those are suffering, a nice idea is to spruce them up—maybe plant a

little herb garden or tomato plants. Any little spoonful of assistance is very helpful.

9) *Gift basket ideas*—A good hospital-stay theme would be comfy pajamas (get the kind that button down the front), bathrobe, a funny book or magazines, warm nonslip socks or slippers, eye mask, and earplugs. One for recovery might have some funny movies, popcorn, and a fleece blanket. Coworkers could get together and give a juicer, recipes for juicing, and some ingredients. Another group gift idea is a weekend away—book a hotel or spa or rent a beach house. Most patients are reeling financially as well as emotionally. Having cancer is expensive. They may not feel it's in their budget to treat themselves to a well-deserved, relaxing break.

Home after Surgery

Let me tell you something you already know. The world ain't all sunshine and rainbows. It is a very mean and nasty place and it will beat you to your knees and keep you there permanently if you let it. You, me, or nobody is gonna hit as hard as life. But it ain't how hard you hit; it's about how hard you can get hit, and keep moving forward. How much you can take, and keep moving forward. That's how winning is done.

—Rocky Balboa

I'm selfish, impatient, and a little insecure. I make mistakes, I am out of control and at times hard to handle. But if you can't handle me at my worst, then you sure as hell don't deserve me at my best.

—Marilyn Monroe

Well, to sum up recovery, I was sick and tired of being sick and tired. It is draining, and there aren't a lot of options. I was reminded to keep a long-term perspective—figure it would take two years to get to "normal." Of course, this won't be my old normal, but a new normal for me.

When I felt especially drained, I would just take a moment, close my eyes and remember what I already knew—I am strong and will get through. I also knew it would get a bit worse before it got better, since chemotherapy was looming as the next step. But one step at a time, one foot in front of the other.

When I returned home from the hospital, I was on a pain medication, a laxative, and strict orders to take it easy and report any aches, pains, or unusual symptoms immediately. One of my nurses was kind enough to give me her cell phone number and said I could call her directly with any concerns, anytime. It was a relief to have her as a resource. My insurance company called to let me know some of the benefits I was entitled to. This was an unexpected and pleasant surprise. They let me know I qualified to have a home nurse visit weekly for nine weeks to check out my incisions, take my vitals, and answer any questions. One of the other benefits my insurance company informed me of was that I had a wig allowance of $350. I didn't expect that either; I never thought of hair as a prosthetic.

My first couple of weeks after surgery are a bit hazy. My main concern was to keep everything as normal and on schedule as possible. Recognizing Maggie and Jane's childhood was coming to a screeching halt with our divorce and my diagnosis, I wanted to cushion my daughters as much as possible. I was extraordinarily thankful they were in school during the day and that the days were getting a little longer and a little warmer. These are the days those of us who live in New England cherish after our long winters. My father was playing in an international masters' tennis tournament in California, so my parents had to leave the day after I got home from surgery. (My father and uncle would place first in doubles!) Stephanie stayed with us that weekend. A working mother of four daughters, she put everything on hold, showing up with a magical bag that kept bringing forth everything we would need for sustenance in the coming days—homemade soups and sauces, cookies, magazines, books, a beautiful warm sweater, flowers, and healthy snacks.

Monday I was on my own. Dr. Cusick called to say he had looked over the surgery reports and was happy with the results.

"Looks like everything worked out just about as well as it possibly could. I'm planning on getting an invitation to your hundredth birthday party."

"Absolutely—I'll bake the cake!"

"Please let me know if you need anything at all. Take good care." I could hear in his voice how happy and relieved he was.

"Thank you for everything. I really appreciate all that you did to help see me through."

That week I woke up every morning and saw my girls off to the bus stop. Then I would head back to sleep until the school bus delivered my girls back to me, taking short breaks for nourishment and drugs. Unsalted almonds, green tea, chicken soup, pasta—mostly bland comfort food was what tasted good to me, and I tried to get in fiber, proteins, and an array of vitamins and minerals. I discovered diet plum juice is pretty good and has a fair amount of fiber and antioxidants. I wish I had my juicer then, since that would have made getting a variety of nutrients easier. Getting my system moving was still an issue for me and would be for almost a full two weeks. Fortunately I finally got my pipes unclogged and fully operational. It was quite a relief.

I did the after-school routines of dance classes and piano lessons and play dates and horseback riding and dinner, and Maggie and I played an extraordinary number of domino games—then early to bed. I was trying to get us back to the sanctity of our normal. I was fortunate I could put my job on hold and just concentrate on getting healthy and taking care of my family. I am in awe of those who recover while working full time. As I mentioned, there may be insurance benefits if you feel you need to take a brief leave from your job to put your full energy and concentration into healing.

Maggie and Jane were on their best behavior—helpful, caring, and polite—totally worried about me. I would go into each of their bedrooms and kiss them good night; do my bedtime routine of brushing teeth, washing face, putting lotion on my incisions, and making sure I had my prescriptions and some water near my bedside. I would roll gingerly into bed, wrap my left side in pillows, turn out the lights, and within the thirty seconds it took for me to fall asleep, my door would creak open, and Jane would tiptoe in and crawl into bed with me. She was careful to stay near the opposite edge, so I might not realize her presence. Within an hour I would be awakened to her limbs in my space, her soft snoring and night breath close to my face and her warmth and worry blanketing me. Regularly Maggie would come down from her third-floor bedroom, and I would stir, scootch over, reposition Jane, and make room for her—just like we did when they were very young. I got to be the inside part of the sandwich. It was almost impossible to sleep but hard not to love. It was a healing strength my little beings brought to bear as they ensconced me in my sleep.

Like a snowflake, and cancer itself, recovery is an individually unique matter. I struggled to climb the stairs, taking them one at a time, partially pulling myself up with both hands gripping the banister. I had flashbacks of my Grampa Van hoisting himself upstairs the same way and could imagine the fatigue and weightiness of my bones having the same feel as an octogenarian. I struggled to stay awake and alert from the school bus arriving at two thirty until eight thirty, which seemed a totally reasonable time to go to sleep. I struggled with cramps and numbness around my surgery site—and still do, although less frequently. They are similar to the charley horses we have all had in our calves at night and happen sometimes when I bend down and then can't straighten as a knot of muscle and nerves and tightness around my ribs holds me rigid.

I struggled with being debilitated and was impatient with my slow recovery.

I was very thankful for my medical team, my family and friends, and all the support I received making getting back to our routine possible.

Not everyone is going to be able to know how to best encourage and assist you. There is a fair amount of wisdom-mongering that goes around with a diagnosis.

True story—a friend was over one day and told me how she couldn't find a parking spot and needed to park a mile from her appointment. She was late, it started to rain, she couldn't find an umbrella, and her thought was, "This must be how Karen feels. This is a really bad day. I am having a Karen day." It's hard for me to become speechless, but it turns out, not impossible. She laughed while she told me her woes, and I became transfixed with studying her Adam's apple going up and down between her guffaws. Really? You got a little wet and were a few minutes late, and you thought somehow that must be how I feel? This was after Brian died, my daughters were struggling, I was bald from chemotherapy treatments, reconciling with living with most of my left lung gone, and trying to sell our home to pay for everything. There are cures and treatments for a lot of things, but no cure for stupid. People will say stupid things to you. Most mean well, I think—I hope—it's just hard maybe for some to work out how to articulate their concern. Try to be forgiving.

Some people, many friends even, have not yet met their life's challenge(s); most will at some point, but it is hard to understand what you are experiencing. I preferred to back-burner or deep-six relationships I knew would be a drain to me. You will be amazed by friends you were close to who will disappear, some for selfish reasons, some somewhat understandably. You will be blessed by acquaintances who step up and are strong and helpful. Your priorities will change. My patience for people who complain about walking in the rain without an umbrella is very limited.

Good support can come through in many ways. If your family and friends are not available, there are many volunteers eager to help you. Reach out to me if you have any questions – I'd be happy to help out if I can. I'm putting in some references of volunteer organizations at the back of the book, don't be uncomfortable in the least about calling, that's what they are there for.

I am blessed with a family that is a treasure nonpareil. My parents and brother were indispensible to me. My sister, Jill, three thousand miles away, sent gift boxes and cards and treats. Jill even made me a warm fleece blanket I would have indulged in more if my daughters were not wrapped in it continually.

I'm incredibly fortunate to be part of a wide-reaching covey of cousins who are simply the best. Julie sent me reassuring medical analyses and packed up all of her mother's caps worn throughout her rounds of chemotherapy. She mailed scores of notes and funny cards and sent me good juju. Her family lined us up with an excellent gourmet-meal plan the girls took great enjoyment ordering from and sampling. My cousin Katherine sent poems and texts and letters. Other cousins sent along cards of encouragement and prayers and well wishes. Aunts and uncles called and visited and sent gift cards and notes of comfort and fortitude. I was awash in compassion and generosity.

I was also supported by my high school gang. Many I had only seen once or twice since college. They made me realize how true the saying is about keeping the old, golden friends. Something about those teenaged years bonds in a way no other time of life can make up for. We enjoyed our fair share of misadventures as Crescent Valley High School Raiders, radiating casual disrespect for authority and utter lack of regard for risk. It is a wonder that not only did we survive the times; we all grew up to be somewhat respectable and accomplished and upstanding. At least somewhat.

It was heartwarming how much community support we got right away from our town. It is touching to have so many sign up to help. Something about cancer impacts each of us personally, as most of our lives are affected one way or another by cancer.

I got loads of information and a feeling of community by joining Inspire. com. Cancer is impossible to describe; even most doctors treating you don't know what it's like, and it has carved us into a different, often kinder community. These compatriots know firsthand the rigors experienced and will give honest, compassionate answers and encouragement; this is combat candor. This is a gift. They will embolden you, touch your life, and help shape your journey.

It's important, though, to remember these compatriots have health histories that cannot be fully known, and some along the way will stop being available. Do you remember the *Peanuts* show about Charlie Brown competing in the spelling bee? I've always been a little disturbed by the part when all the kids' faces appear in bubbles, and as they misspell a word, their bubble pops and they disappear from the screen. The faces of those in the trenches with us disappear from time to time, replaced by new ones seeking answers and tips learned along the way.

A few years ago, one of my aunts was ill, and I sent her the top-ten funniest movies of all time, according to the "experts." The discs were then sent on to an uncle who was recovering from surgery, who in turn forwarded them to another aunt recovering from an operation, and they found their way full circle back to me. My friend Tracy sent me a whole set of funny joke CDs we would listen to in the car. And I got videos and cards and funny e-mails. I loved them all. The benefits of laughing are extensive. The physical benefits include increased levels of endorphins and dopamine, a physiological sense of lowered stress and pain. Emotionally one feels less depressed, anxious, and tense, as well as more hopeful, energetic, and optimistic. We made sure we had a good laugh every day.

Music is another great and easy way to boost your spirits. I played Pandora stations that made me want to dance in the afternoons. I didn't always feel up to dancing, and when I did shake my groove thing, it was never outwardly fully appreciated by my audience. But I think if teens don't get the opportunity to roll their eyes at least daily, it might lead to some sort of astigmatism. My grooving around the kitchen gave us all the sense we were going to be okay. It was hard for me to focus on the simple fact that these were also the days of my life and had to be *lived* as much as possible. *Every single day counts.*

At night I put on soothing music or a meditation app. A friend told me of a phone app, HeadSpace, a free ten-minute guided meditation series I listened to almost every night. It's a relaxing way to end the day and to do a quick check on how your body is feeling. The narrator has a soothing British accent. I am a sucker for a guy with a cool accent.

The Tuesday morning following my discharge, Stephanie picked me up, and we headed back to the Brigham for another CT scan and follow-up with Dr. TG. The Brigham and Women's Hospital is immense and different wings are reached by way of the Richard Nessen Pike, or what everyone calls simply "the Pike." Just like the throughway the Mass Pike, this is a busy thoroughfare. The BWH Pike is located on the second floor and is one of the busiest hallways I have ever seen, stretching blocks and bustling with doctors, patients, wheelchairs, food carts, and every medical apparatus one could possibly imagine. We were directed to the imaging department, located midway along the Pike. Once there I filled out a questionnaire, double-checked my insurance and contact information was accurate, and after a short wait was escorted in for my CT scan. Quick and easy. Afterward we proceeded a short way down the Pike to Dr. TG's office. The nurse took my vitals including weight (down three pounds), blood pressure (127/89), temperature (97), pulse (93), and oxygen saturation (100 percent). Oxygen-saturation levels should be between 96 and 100 percent. A clip is placed on the index finger that monitors the amount of hemoglobin filled with oxygen molecules. Obviously, your body needs oxygen in order to function. Anything below 90 percent can mean respiratory failure—not a good sign. The test is easy and painless.

The nurse asked me if I was a smoker and questioned how I was doing and what pain level I was feeling as she pointed at that familiar doctor's office chart of the red, grimacing faces at 10 to the ebullient 1 faces. I did learn in recovery that a 4 is the threshold nursing staff needed in order to justify pain medication. I told the nurse I felt I was between a 2 and a 3 that day. She then checked my stitches and sent me along to the next room to see Dr. TG.

Stephanie, my superlative wingman, wrote down my vitals in my journal right away. She added the fact that my pulse was ninety-three, even with the Ativan I had taken that morning to take the edge off the uneasiness I felt about this first important follow up. She noted my temperature may have been influenced by Motrin and Tylenol. Excellent detail gal.

I was asked to put on the blue gown, and we waited while my chest scan taunted us from the computer screen. There are too many shadows and features and suspicious shapes for a CT-scan-reading neophyte, and I grew increasingly uneasy about them while left in a room with few distractions, save the lung depicted in multiple shades of gray on the monitor. Irrespective of fabulous company, it was impossible for me not to get absorbed into studying its white-to-gray-shaded tones. I plan on asking the image not be left up for me to wonder about. I wish I had enough nerve to turn the computer screen off.

Dr. TG knocked and entered, giving me a warm handshake.

"How are you feeling?" He asked like he truly wanted to know. I appreciate that.

"Pretty well."

Then he turned and sat and studied the image.

"Your lungs look great. See the left side, here? That's the lower left lung moving up to fill in the space left by the upper lobe being removed. And down here is your stomach that has moved over a bit. The air pocket is gone now. Your lower lung has fully expanded and looks great. Everything looks good."

He turned and smiled proudly at me.

"How's the pain been?"

"Well, I've had some cramping and trouble sleeping, but I take the oxycodone when I wake up."

"Any other symptoms?"

"I have some night sweats, and my arms and hands get tingly while I sleep. Sometimes I can get them to wake up if I shake them out; other times it just stays. It can get uncomfortable. My sinus seems swollen around my nose, and my right eye feels like there's a sty in it. I also had been up with diarrhea at night, and Dr. Cusick suggested I stop taking laxatives at nighttime. I spoke with the nurse about it too, and she told me to go off of both the Lactalose and the Senna for a few days and take Colace instead."

I don't think I would have ever remembered all those symptoms if I didn't have my handy journal, which I wrote in every day.

"How has that been?"

"Well, I haven't had any more diarrhea, but I also haven't had a bowel movement since I switched yesterday, so I don't think it is the right combination yet."

"Okay. Let's give it a day or so and see what happens. Give the nurse a call tomorrow, and give her an update. Call me if you get concerned, but it is just going to take a bit for your body to get back on track. We will figure it out."

Dr. TG then checked out my incisions and took the thread out of the stitches at the base of my neck. I had some pain in the area; it felt like there was a hard nodule underneath the thread, which he said was just some scar tissue working itself out.

"CVS will have Mederma, which you might put on your incisions twice a day or after every shower to help with scarring. Also you might try using a loofah to exfoliate the area."

Stephanie dutifully wrote down all the comments and suggestions into my journal.

"So you have a good prognosis. I still believe you should have a discussion about chemotherapy. Having the adjutant treatment will lower your chance of recurrence even more. I have a colleague at Dana Farber I can put you in contact with if you'd like."

"Sure thing. I am willing to do anything I can to improve my odds. Thank you."

"Okay. I will see you again in two weeks. Just make an appointment on your way out."

With a hearty two-handed handshake and smiles all around, my first follow-up post-op was done.

First Post Op CAT results.

IMPRESSION:

Support devices: None
Lungs and pleura: Postsurgical changes seen in the left apex.
There has been significant improvement in left apical pneumothorax now small in size. The right lung is clear.
Retrocardiac opacity slightly increased most in keeping with atelectasis.

Cardiomediastinal silhouette: The cardiomediastinal silhouette is unremarkable.

Tips for Post-Op

1) *Rest.* This was hard and frustrating for me, because I was eager to get back to life as usual. Remember to keep a long-term perspective and know the best thing you can give your body right now is a nap.

2) *Eat.* Your body is going to need fuel to heal. Keep track of what you are eating. There are easy ways to do this with apps on your phone or online programs. I like SparkPeople.com. It is free, has a lot of advice, and you can track your food. It will show all the nutrients you have eaten, so it's easy to see how you are doing and what your body may need. Stick to healthy stuff—whole foods, legumes, grains. We all know how to eat well and steer clear of the junk. No processed foods or fast food or anything that has an ingredient you can't pronounce.

3) *Take care of your scars.* Mederma, vitamin E, cocoa butter, and raw aloe directly from the plant are good options. I had a reaction from the Mederma; it sort of burned a little and made my skin itchy. It's also pretty expensive. But it does work well for many people.

4) *Do not rush recovery.* This can be hard. I just wanted to get back to my "real life" and be done with being sick. I grew annoyed that my body would not accommodate my schedule. It took me a while to realize I needed to adjust my timetable and slow down a little. By "a little," I mean basically to a standstill. Adjust to years, not days or weeks. Slow and steady.

5) *Do not feel guilty.* It may be hard to rest and relax and concentrate on recuperation. Give yourself a pass. Be unapologetically selfish for one year. Enjoy the slow summer days, the colors of fall, the warm fireside books in winter, and the rites of spring. By this point, you have earned it.

6) *Write thank-you notes.* When you feel up to it, you might take a minute and send a quick thank-you note or a basket to your caregivers, nurses,

and doctors. If you grew up as I did, before e-mails and texts, thank-you notes were *de rigeur*. I figure if I send a neighbor a thank-you card for taking care of dogs and plants when we go away for a weekend, why not a handwritten card to the medical team for taking care of my life?

7) *Exercise.* What? Well, I am putting the term out there pretty loosely. Brian hoisted the treadmill from the recesses of the basement to the family room. It was an eyesore for sure but a constant reminder that I needed to move. My journal says that one week after I was released from the hospital, that Friday I walked for five minutes at a pace of one mile an hour. My notes say I felt winded and tired. It was a start. By Tuesday I was walking fifteen minutes at 1.5 miles per hour. My notes say I felt okay. A few months later I was walking an hour at 4.5 miles an hour and doing hot yoga. Baby steps. Just need to start and try to do a little more every day.

8) *Get a massage.* First off, I love to get a massage. Secondly, post surgery it really helps. I know a great masseuse, and she was able to get some of the scar tissue and sore muscles around my surgery site ameliorated. Dana Farber recommends massage as part of recovery. If you don't have a massage place nearby, or it's not in your budget, suggest to your significant other to brush up on the techniques and get some body oils. Relax and enjoy.

Tips for the Team

1) *Start up the food train.* I was so thankful to have some meals taken care of. We even got a few new favorite recipes in the mix. It was also fun to see what was in the containers, mini-culinary Christmases. Concentrate on organic ingredients, and toss in a salad or fruits with the casserole. Remember to double check for any food allergies.

2) *Volunteer to drive the kids to after-school activities.* A patient still on pain medication is not supposed to drive, so offers for chauffeuring are a great help.

3) *Drop off a little something at her doorstep.* Among my favorite things was coming home and discovering a friend had dropped off a disc of soothing music or a candle or a card or cookies or flowers, just left at the front door—so thoughtful and appreciated. If you do send flowers, it's especially nice in the form of a plant or in a vase. Finding and cleaning vases may actually be daunting to someone just home from the hospital.

4) *Do not ring the doorbell unless you are expected.* And if you do visit, keep it short. I remember a few friends who stayed too long. It may have only been twenty minutes total. I wish I could have had the stamina to visit with them all day. I was just wiped out. I remember after one visit—which I thoroughly enjoyed but I felt lasted too long—my whole day's schedule seemed off. In order to keep my forward motion, I rested while the girls were in school. Even twenty minutes of unscheduled activity put me behind, and I was exhausted the rest of the day. Better to visit in small doses for a bit.

Deciding on Chemotherapy

Life has many ways of testing a person's will, either by having nothing happen at all or by having everything happen all at once.

—Paulo Coelho

You have been told that, even like a chain, you are as weak as your weakest link.
This is but half the truth.
You are also as strong as your strongest link.
To measure you by your smallest deed is to reckon the power of the ocean by the frailty of its foam.
To judge you by your failures is to cast blame upon the seasons for their inconstancy.

—Khalil Gibran

The word *chemotherapy* was coined by German chemist Paul Erlich in the early 1900s. He used the term as an all-encompassing word meaning "the use of chemicals to treat disease." The father of modern chemotherapy and one of the namesakes of The Dana Farber Hospital is Sidney Farber. Dr. Farber was born in 1903 in upstate New York, the third of fourteen kids. By the time he was getting around to going to college, he discovered many universities in the United States wouldn't admit a Jewish student, so he started out studying at the Universities of Heidelberg and Freiburg in Germany. He excelled there and was accepted as a transfer student at Harvard University Medical School to complete his degree.

From what I have read, Dr. Farber was a bit of an odd duck. He toiled away as a pediatric pathologist in a small room near the bathrooms, tucked away in the bowels of the Children's Hospital in Boston. He focused his work on the causes of cancer deaths in kids, most particularly leukemia. If you have ever been pregnant, you may remember taking folic acid to help in the development of your baby's bone marrow, where blood cells are made. Dr. Farber got the idea if an *anti*-folic acid could be developed, there may be a way to stop the proliferation of the blood cells that cause leukemia. And he was right. Dr. Farber showed Aminopterin blocked a crucial chemical reaction needed for DNA replication, limiting blood-cell development. This discovery led to remissions in children with acute leukemia. Aminopterin is the predecessor of methotrexate, a cancer-treatment drug commonly used today. Researchers began focusing on drugs that block different functions in cell growth and replication. The modern age of chemotherapy was born.

It unsettles me to ride up the elevators at Dana Farber, the doors opening up to different floors each with signs proclaiming treatment for cancers of every conceivable part of the body. Cancer has become as common as clouds and dust. Each floor heralds indescribable anguish and pain and sorrow, as well as unimaginable courage and strength and care. We are a sorority and fraternity of fighters, with Dana Farber our ring. We go back for each round, the bell of the elevator door signaling our impending knockout, and then back to our respective corners to be cared for by our team and nourished and made to rest a while. I am in awe of the youngest of our gladiators—the six-year-old boy with his irrepressible grin and bald head and swollen body, pleading with his mom to be able to push the button and eagerly standing on tiptoes to reach it so the doors will open up onto his floor and his fight. The beleaguered mom gives a small, tender smile at this brief burst of normalcy as she wheels her son's oxygen tank to the corner of the elevator, squares her shoulders, and gets ready to take as much of the burden from her child as she can. The most powerful of human emotions, love and fear, radiate from her and leave a palpable trail as the pair disembarks. There is nothing I can imagine harder than having your child presented with a life-threatening illness. I sometimes think of that—that as the X was not drawn on our door and we were not passed over, I want it to be me to answer the knock and take the cancer handed out. My fight is infinitely easier than the moms with their kids who just want to get to push the elevator button.

The door opens for my round. My sister, Jill, and I get off on the ninth floor, its sign heralding Thoracic Cancer Treatment. I am troubled and impressed by the further division of treatment. There are tracheal and thymus and tumors on chest walls, and there are mesothelioma and mediastinal and metastatic tumors to the lungs. It overwhelms and shocks and impresses.

Twenty percent of lung cancer patients are now women like me—nonsmokers with no family history. It is the only subgroup of cancer on the rise. In fact, lung cancer in nonsmokers would rank number six in fatal cancers in the United States if given its own category. Roughly 65 percent of all new cases of lung cancer are from those who have *never* smoked or who stopped decades ago. Experts don't know why there is this sudden surge and are testing hypotheses such as cleaning products and foods and beauty regimens.

The only criterion needed in order to be diagnosed with lung cancer is to have lungs.

I am guilty of adding the fact I am a nonsmoker when questioned about my lung cancer. I guess I feel somehow entitled to more sympathy or more righteousness or a greater sense of injustice. The statistics are scary. What Dr. TG told me when I questioned him about the mortality rates resonates with me. He said simply it does not matter at all if it's 5 percent or 16.6 percent or 30 percent or 99 percent. I have to be 100 percent of me. I am not going to shed any percentage but forge ahead at 0 percent or 100 percent.

Choose.

Some, surprisingly to me, choose 0 percent. Some simply feel the Genghis Khan nature of cancer and surrender at the news of the impending battle, assuming defeat is imminent. Stephanie's mom didn't want to go through chemotherapy for breast cancer because she didn't want to lose her hair; she didn't want people to know she was afflicted with the disease. She died at fifty-five before she could meet her four beautiful granddaughters. Another friend told me the heartbreaking story of a neighbor who was blessed with six children. Four of them died of cancer. When the fourth became afflicted, a mother of two young children, she opted not to go through the fight, fearing the same outcome as her three siblings and not wanting to endure the battle.

I know we all have stories, and it is sometimes hard to comprehend why people make the choices they do. Each has to do what she feels is best for her own life journey. I never thought of my fight as a choice. I decided immediately to beat my cancer.

Decide is a powerful word. The definition is "come to a decision in the mind as a result of consideration; cause to come to a resolution." *Resolve,* "to decide firmly on a course of action." *Commit,* "pledge or bind to a certain cause or policy." These words are mighty and strong and forceful. Forge these three words into a braid and use them as your back brace, for there will be days when you will need to rely on them. I know they are not enough, but they are a good place to start. Start by deciding, resolving, committing to be the 100 percent. Don't question the outcome. Know it will be hard. Know it may come close to killing you. Know you will be 100 percent of you.

●————————————————●

My Dana Farber oncologist reminds me of Jim Carrey—same immense, toothy smile and wide-eyed, strenuous joviality. He has a frenetic evangelical way about him. I often have a hard time feeling he is taking my cancer seriously. But as he was handpicked by Dr. TG, I feel confident he is competent and capable. At our first meeting, Bruce Almighty met me exuberantly, going over my chart and tapping away at the computer.

"This program shows us exactly what your odds are. It doesn't pool all the lung cancer patients together. So let's see. Female. Forty-seven years old. Excellent health. Stage 2. No mets. No lymph node involvement.

Tumor of about five centimeters. And voila! You have a 75 percent chance of making it five years, 80 percent if you do chemotherapy." He was enthusiastic about this news. I imagine it may have been the best stats he had given all day. I guess it's all about perspective, but after the tumor was removed and I learned the lymph nodes were clear and there was no other sign of cancer anywhere, I figured I was sort of back to at least somewhere around 90 percent at least and chemo would get me to 99.9 percent—since there are no absolutes, especially with health, but definitely get me back to the pool of generally healthy people. There's something immediately tangible about surgery. The results are obvious—like mowing the lawn and washing the windows and cleaning your plate. A concrete before and after, and I thought I was more, well, *after.*

I was devastated. My sister's reaction was probably more in line with what Dr. Carrey was expecting.

"Okay! That's great news, right?" Jill was supportive and upbeat.

I felt sideswiped.

"I'd like to get you started on four rounds of chemotherapy over the next ten weeks. You will come in every three weeks for a combination of Cisplatin and Alimta. These are tough drugs and will get the job done, but it may be they are a bit rough to keep on schedule, so we will carefully monitor how your body is handling them and may need to slow down the timing."

"All right. It sounds as though it makes sense to do it now." I didn't want to ever look back and feel I had not done everything I possibly could to avoid a recurrence. "I have some questions too." I reached for my journal.

"Next time! Next time!" Dr. Carrey was the picture of the Doorknob Doc, one hand on the handle, already headed out. My allotted time was up. "See you again in a few weeks!" And with the cheeriest of waves, he bounced from the room.

"I guess we'll leave those other questions for the next visit," I said with an exasperated laugh to Jill as she closed up my journal and handed it back to me.

Jill is five years younger than I am, and we have not spent much time together as adults. She was still in middle school when I left for college, and we've lived on opposite sides of the country since she graduated from high school. Jill is a fabulous baker and the mother of two amazing children. She has a kind, smart, and accomplished husband and a beautiful home. I was very happy to have her come out and help see us through one of the segments along the journey. It is one of the silver linings to cancer: you get to spend more time with family.

I struggled with the fact that chemotherapy increased my chance of surviving lung cancer for five years by only 5 percent. It just doesn't sound like a lot for the amount of effort and strife and hair. I pictured myself in a room with one hundred people and thought five seemed like a bigger number if life itself was what was at stake. I don't know why, but I pictured a round table and there are four of me sitting around it playing cards, drinking wine, listening to music, and enjoying great conversation, having some laughs. Then Fate walks in and plays a little duck, duck, death and taps one of us on the shoulder. This me reluctantly puts down her cards and with a wistful wave leaves the room. I imagine myself being at a table of four and at a table of five. I don't like the odds either way, but I know which one I prefer.

I opted for the chemotherapy.

Jill and I headed to the waiting room to be called to check in with the chemotherapy unit. Despite its plush surroundings and large picture window running the length of a wall, giving a glimpse of Fenway Park, it is a somber, quiet, echoey place—a way station that reminds me of the Land of Misfit Toys. I saw women with bald heads, patients attached to oxygen tanks via tubes plugging up their nostrils, many wearing surgical masks in an attempt to reduce exposure to the germs that might further weaken their immune systems and resolve. These people are my tribe. We were all waiting to be called for our chance to be put back together and made whole again by the doctors and surgeons and chemicals.

I texted Stephanie the statistics I was given. My phone immediately rang.

"What the f—ck! 75 percent, 80 percent *with* chemo? You only get 5 percent extra to go through that?" She was outraged.

I began to sob. "I know. It's not what I expected. I thought I was *done*."

I glanced around the room, embarrassed to be openly crying. Patients were casting uncomfortable looks my way. I am certain my terror resonated with them. I met the eye of one member of my new clan. He appeared in bad shape, I must say. He was attached to an oxygen tank, a grayish tint accentuating his weathered skin and baldness. We looked at each other, and time stood still for me. His eyes spoke of a hard journey and little hope. He held my gaze for a few heartbeats and then turned back to his magazine, his slumped shoulders folding in over his worn frame. He was here, in our ring, going back for another round. He was still fighting for the promise held up by the science and doctors and drugs; still holding out for victory against the odds. I became annoyed and a little ashamed with myself. I had a good prognosis. My guess is I probably received one of the best prognoses in the room, and I was making my other tribe members uncomfortable with my crying. I was strong and could do this. I had hope. I had more than hope; I had conviction. I tried to get myself together a little, find perspective. I was not going to let my tribe down.

I discovered I could get to a place inside myself where I can go when I feel buried by stress and uncertainty – it's sort of a meditation thing. I take a minute to just clear my head and feel I'm standing still behind a latched door, keeping out the storm. I simply breathe and be by myself for a while—sometimes just for a second, a second of stillness, where I am calm and everything around me is silent for a moment. Just long enough to give me strength, to remember I am still here; I am still alive. I am capable. I can do this. I wait for the storm of my thoughts, fears, feelings, doubts, and the overwhelming-ness to pass before unlatching the door and taking stock of the chaos of Life.

I concentrated on my game plan. One step at a time. Chemotherapy was my next step toward complete recovery. I didn't have time to indulge in doubt. I had a mission to complete.

Breathe in, breathe out. Repeat.

I thought I would be starting chemotherapy right then and there, but my appointment was simply to get my height and weight so the chemotherapy dosage would be spot-on for my frame. The nursing staff could not have been more kind and patient. I was given a little tour of the infusion area and got a chance to check out the comfortable lounging seats with the footrests and the views the ultra-large windows gave of the Boston neighborhood. I felt like the new recruit with the veterans in their chairs, books in hand or knitting, many with the headscarf covering their heads, some napping. I would soon be going through this rite of passage on my way to becoming a full-fledged cancer team survivor member.

We stopped in at Dr. TG's office after my initial interview with the chemotherapy staff. An Indian gentleman was interning with him and came in to go over my scans and to see if I had any questions.

"I just heard these statistics that were a little scary to me." I still needed reassurance.

"Oh, not to worry. Don't worry about statistics. You see, those other patients, they did not have your Dr. TG." He was grinning and giving me an endearing head bobble that made me smile. I relaxed a bit.

"There are patients in the waiting room right now who have been here for five years. Some for ten." Grinning bobble.

That's not what I wanted to hear. I was the single mother of an eleven- and twelve-year-old. Five years, even ten, was not that reassuring.

I tried to keep the smile on my face, as I knew he was doing his best to be optimistic.

Dr. TG walked in and replaced him. "How are you feeling?" he asked as he shook my hand.

"I feel well. A little sore still, but I am a bit nervous about the statistics Dr. Carrey just gave me—75 percent chance of five years, 80 percent with chemo?"

Dr. TG sat down and looked at me seriously, and this is when he gave me the stats chat. "I wish doctors wouldn't give statistics. They do not mean a thing. You are not going to be 75 percent or 80 percent of you; you will be 100 percent. Look—I saw how you were through the operation, through the recovery, and now. I am not a prophet, but I am telling you right now—you are going to be fine."

I exhaled and felt hope again.

"Have you ever seen the statistics of driving in Boston? Or flying on a plane?" He was coaxing the point home.

"Hey, I'm driving into Boston and getting on a flight tomorrow!" Jill interjected.

"Well, there are risks with everything. We all have to just take it one day at a time and enjoy life while we can."

He then checked my stitches, my scans, and my chart and declared I was healthy.

I texted Stephanie. *So here's the thing. My two floor items have not been breached. Maggie and Jane have clear lungs and my cancer did not metastasize to my brain. Those were the two things I would not be able to manage well. The chemotherapy and the statistics are beyond that. I can do this. One day at a time.*

She replied right away. *I am in awe of how quickly you came around to that. And you are right. The floor is still there and we move on from that.*

Tips for Deciding on Chemotherapy

1) *Know your limits.* Chemotherapy is hard, both physically and emotionally. People decide for and against chemo for a multitude of personal reasons. Make sure you are comfortable with the decision you make. Also bear in mind it's hard but endurable. We do make it through.

2) *Interview oncologists and get opinions.* I didn't interview; I just took Dr. TG's referral, since I have the utmost faith in him. Dr. Carrey does have a team of oncologists at Dana Farber who meet and discuss cases and weigh in on treatment plans. I was told in my case it was a unanimous opinion that I ought to go ahead with chemotherapy. If you are on the fence, I would get advice from a few oncologists as to whether they feel chemotherapy would make a significant enough difference for the distress to be worthwhile. The surgery, radiation, or other means of ridding your body of the cancer or stopping its growth might be all that is needed in your case.

Tips for the Team

1) *Listen.*

2) *Listen.*

3) *Listen.*

Chemotherapy

The harder the conflict, the more glorious the triumph. What we obtain too cheap, we esteem too lightly; it is dearness only that gives everything its value. I love the man that can smile in trouble, that can gather strength from distress and grow.

—Thomas Paine

Man often becomes what he believes himself to be. If I keep on saying to myself that I cannot do a certain thing, it is possible that I may end by really becoming incapable of doing it. On the contrary, if I have the belief that I can do it, I shall surely acquire the capacity to do it even if I may not have it at the beginning.

—Mahatma Gandhi

I started Cisplatin and Alimta on April 22, 2013, at Dana Farber Hospital, having waited the requisite eight weeks deemed necessary for my body to be strong enough to handle the onslaught after surgery.

Although Cisplatin has been around since the mid 1800's, the FDA approved its use as a chemotherapy drug fairly recently, in 1978. Basically Cisplatin reminds our DNA to get back to doing its job – to put the brakes on our cancer cells and get them to commit cell hari-kari. Cisplatin has been nicknamed "Cis-flatten" by nurses because it is so tough on patients. Recipients used to average twelve vomits a day while being treated with this platinum-based drug. Cisplatin's powerful punch has been diluted somewhat by potent antinausea drugs now administered in combination. I like that it's also referred to as the "penicillin of cancer" and is a tried-and-true staple of treatment. Carboplatin is often substituted, as its toxicity is lower, and therefore the side effects are less severe. A recent study cited in the *Journal of the National Cancer Institute* shows Cisplatin is a preferred drug to use on early-stage lung cancer where a cure is the focus, and Carboplatin is recommended for later stages, to get the disease under control without risking the additional complications associated with Cis-flatten.

Dana Farber is truly an extraordinary facility. The staff is the rare combination of competent and kind. Volunteers push around carts offering books, magazines, and newspapers; others give hand massages, crackers, sandwiches, and beverages. Nutritionists stop by to go over your diet, clergy visit and ask if they can pray for you, and the barf bags are super cool. They look like miniature vacuum cleaner bags with rigid tops. I tucked a few away in my bag for the girls. A big hit.

Of course, I was there getting chemotherapy, so there's that piece of it too. I called chemo "Magic Potion" to my kids. It was easier for me to think of it that way, rather than the deadly cocktail it was, bringing me to the brink of bodily shutdown every three weeks. I tried to visualize the Magic Potion as an airy, soft, rose-colored mist, but somehow images of black, luminous Death Eaters coursing through my body, destroying everything in their path, was all I could envision.

As the Magic Potion flowed into my veins and traveled throughout my body on its search-and-destroy mission of all rapidly dividing cells, I looked out over the Fens and a beautiful spring view of Boston. Fenway Park's lights were off but would be turned on later as the Red Sox took on the Orioles. I was lucky enough to be in Boston when the eighty-six-year Curse of the Bambino was broken and the Red Sox finally won the world championship in 2004. Their previous World Series win on September 4, 1918, is forever immortalized by four of the retired numbers displayed in right field—number 9 (Ted Williams), number 4 (Joe Cronin), number 1 (Bobby Doerr), and number 8 (Carl Yastrzemski). As exciting as the 2004 World Series was, the playoffs against the Yankees leading up to it is by far the most exciting sports I have ever witnessed.

George Herman Ruth was one of the earliest pioneers in chemotherapy. Of course, most everyone called him Babe. Back in September 1946, Ruth went to the French Hospital in New York City with the left side of his face swollen so badly his eye was completely shut, and he could hardly swallow because his throat was so sore. The doctors originally diagnosed him with a toothache, maybe combined with sinusitis, pulled out three of his teeth, gave him some penicillin, and sent him home.

Ruth didn't get better, and his throat remained so inflamed he was barely able to swallow or speak. He returned to the French Hospital for further tests; this time he had an x-ray that showed a large tumor at the base of his skull. The doctors again misdiagnosed him, this time as afflicted with Horner syndrome. There is little treatment for this syndrome, and the Babe continued having serious problems as he went to various New York hospitals for relief.

Dr. Lewisohn at the Mount Sinai Hospital suggested a chemotherapy drug, Teropterin, which had shown success in mice. Babe volunteered to be the first human to be treated with Teropterin, despite Dr. Lerisohn saying he was not convinced the drug would help, and in fact, might make his condition worse. Ruth wrote, "I realized that if anything was learned about that type of treatment, whether good or bad, it would be of use in the future to the medical profession and maybe to a lot of people with my same trouble." In June 1947, Babe started daily injections of Teropterin, and it seemed to work—his pain went away, his spirits picked up, he was able to eat again, and he began recouping the eighty pounds he had dropped the previous year.

His better health didn't last though and on August 16, 1948, the Sultan of Swat died of pneumonia. He was fifty-three.

The Babe is known for his phenomenal talent in baseball, but arguably his biggest contribution was to the medical community as one of the first to come forward to try experimental chemotherapy. Babe, and tens of thousands more like him, shaped the treatment of cancer.

Chemotherapy has come a long way since the Bambino was treated in 1947. Now drugs are often individualized to one's own particular cancer cells. Sort of like a Pac-Man running around distinguishing a certain shape of cell and just gobbling that particular one up, leaving all the healthy cells to go about their business. My chemo didn't work out that way. I did not get the pick-and-choose type of cell destruction; mine was of the carpet-bombing variety.

Chemotherapy is tough; no way around it. It is ironic to me that I didn't feel sick while I actually had cancer, only during its removal and treatment stages.

I'm not clear why there was no marijuana offered or even discussed. I suppose it mostly helps with patients with weight loss, and the steroids I was on blew me up like a blowfish. It seems to me that the grass may be greener with those patients who lose weight and get the encouragement to indulge in the munchies.

My chemo side effects were not as bad as many. The thing that struck me with chemotherapy is that everything in life seemed muted—colors were not as vivid, sounds were not as sharp, nothing tasted right, and I went through the day in a type of numb haze. I didn't throw up at all, although I was nauseated quite a bit. And I had aversions to things like orange cheese, the smell of pretty much any food cooking, and sour foods and water. I was not hungry but was able to eat—which I did. I made a conscious effort to get good nutrients in and a ton of water, which I flavored with mint, lemon, or cucumbers. I figured my liver and kidneys were overworked processing the poison, and the least I could do was dilute the toxins and keep flushing them away. I arrived at the point where my nurse suggested I may be drinking too much water and could be running the risk of losing electrolytes.

It was a balancing act, one of many.

Chemotherapy is about endurance, and endurance is about strength, patience, and fortitude. Post-infusion days three to ten were the hardest for me, and that seems typical. I felt I had been run over by a bus and then left to race a marathon in neck-high quicksand—uphill ... while being chased by wildebeests.

The third week was a bit of a reprieve, and I started feeling more human, and this made it difficult to go back for the next round. It was hard to voluntarily offer up my arm to the needle that would inject poisons that made me feel like crap for so long.

I had signed up for four rounds.

Common side effects of chemotherapy include constipation, diarrhea, fatigue, hair loss, anemia, bleeding, nausea, vomiting, infertility, infection, nervous-system problems, skin and nail issues, kidney complications, mouth and throat trouble, and hearing difficulties. Oh, and let's not forget the ever-prominent chemo brain.

Chemotherapy drugs attack all cells proliferating quickly. All of the following cells are impacted: hair (why we lose it), stomach (why we go through so much nausea), skin cells (leaving us susceptible to sunburns and skin sensitivity), ovaries (which might mean permanent or temporary menopause or infertility), and red and white blood cells (which leaves us with a suppressed immune system). Not a lot left unscathed.

Wigs and time work for hair loss; medicines offset the constipation and diarrhea; although impossible to shake, sleep is key for fatigue; diet and supplements can help manage anemia; bleeding needs to be monitored by the medical staff; nausea and vomiting—again, time and diet—but mostly time; skin and nails can be helped by lotions and time; kidney function will be monitored closely by the medical team and is often the reason why chemotherapy is cut short. It is a lot for the kidneys to process. Drinking liquids is the biggest help you can give them. Hearing problems are usually mild but can be as severe as some permanent hearing loss. What is most common is a ringing noise called tinnitus. I noticed some tinnitus. It is annoying but doesn't hurt and usually goes away after a few weeks. Mouth and throat are partially dealt with at the time of infusion. It has been found that chewing on ice while infusions are going on helps prevent mouth sores from forming. I feel queasy just thinking of the ice bits I was given. Something about the staleness and the taste of them combined with the nauseated feeling I got during chemo turns my stomach. I did chew on the ice during the first and second rounds but then opted for Popsicles instead. So much better. Or try Fudgsicles. Something frozen with a nice flavor; just don't choose anything you often crave, as you may end up with an aversion to it. Grape Popsicles were the ticket for me. I was also told to gargle with baking soda a few times a day following chemo, to help with mouth inflammation. I ended up with a few mouth sores but nothing that bad.

Dysgeusia (which looks a lot like disgust-ia to me) is another side effect. Basically it translates to mean "a change in the sense of taste," which translates in real-life language to "food is going to taste gross." Almost everyone complains about a metal taste that makes food unpalatable, and beverages too—even water. Some ways to combat this are to eat with plastic utensils, avoid anything canned, and eat bland foods like bananas, rice, potatoes, and pasta. Drink. Many go in for prepared beverages such as Ensure, Gatorade, or Propel that provide a bunch of vitaminerals as well as the liquid needed.

There are many conflicting reports about nutrition and chemotherapy, and recommendations seem to change weekly. Supplements, antioxidants, and multivitamins all bring about hotly debated arguments. I took, and continue to take, vitamin D and fish-oil tablets. Those are my two supplements, and they were cleared by my nutritionist and Dr. Carrey. There is a ton of research coming out on vitamin D's benefits. Who knows? It likely can't hurt. And of course there are those who eschew chemotherapy and head to clinics where carrot juice and coffee enemas are dispensed for cancer. Some say it works. I would try them if Western medicine reached its limits for my cure. I guess I buy into the science and research of chemotherapy, and I feel more comfortable augmenting with herbs and lifestyle changes to enhance the drug regimen. I am not crazy about the idea of a coffee enema, but figure if I tried everything else and still needed help, I would drop trou and give it a go. But that's just me. We each need to decide our own path to take.

Make sure you talk with your doctor about what you are eating and what supplements you take. Better yet, go in and see a nutritionist; there should be one on staff at your hospital, and it's easy to schedule an appointment that coincides with your other follow-up visits. A few recommendations that make sense in general, but especially while going through chemo, are to eat organically whenever possible and to avoid processed foods and sugars and caffeine. Since your immune system is going to be compromised, avoid undercooked meats and fish (no sushi was a bummer for me) and stay away from areas where you may catch something. I guess this is common sense, but if it's winter, you may not want to hang out in crowded areas where you may be exposed to whatever cold is lurking.

I remember going to Jane's fifth grade spelling bee in the high school auditorium. It took place the day after I got home from my operation. I could barely walk across the parking lot and did not sit down because I didn't trust I would be able to summon the strength to stand back up. I just leaned against the back wall and waited for her part of the competition to end. I made certain she saw me and knew I was there cheering her on; then I headed home and collapsed. Probably not the brightest thing to do health-wise. Try not to do that; stay clear of school auditoriums. I'm certain they could be used in pretty much any science experiment for germs and grime and all things a cancer patient is supposed to avoid. Of course, the same may be said for a hospital.

Another symptom is chemo brain. There's not a lot we can do about chemo brain. I sort of think mine started well before treatment, and now when I forget names or addresses or dates, I have a go-to excuse. I am planning on excusing all gaffes to chemo brain from here on out.

I played a bunch of games to keep some blood flow directed to my frontal lobe. I put the Sudoku app on my phone, played Words with Friends around the clock (I am pretty good at it), and joined Lumosity. com, training almost every day and trying to consistently improve my scores. The haze does lift. As with so much of this journey, patience and time are the best possible solutions. I am back to my everyday random searching for names or dates now.

So when you start chemo, dress comfortably and eat a little something before it starts. But steer clear of fatty or greasy foods or anything sugary, as they might add to your upcoming bouts with nausea. As with any time you are having blood drawn or medicine via IV, wear loose-fitting clothes—preferably short sleeves—and something easy to lounge in. Stephanie brought along all sorts of things to entertain us for the eight hours it took to get my blood test, my appointment with Dr. Carrey, and my Magic Potion into my system. We ended up just chatting away, the bag left unattended at our feet as we skimmed through magazines and savored the time with no place to go and nothing to do but to simply enjoy each other's company. It is a rarity for moms not to feel the urge to be accomplishing, whether by producing a cleaner house, a healthy meal, a paycheck, or a child on time (usually a combination of all four at any time during any given day). I was tethered to my comfy chair and made to sit and steep. My nurse, Susie, was terrific. She would pop in on us from time to time to check that the flow of medicine was on track and to change out empty infusion bags for full as needed. She brought blankets for me and replenished our stack of magazines and offered a variety of snacks and drinks from the refrigerator. It was a little like riding first class on a plane—although without the complimentary champagne.

We were told we were finished as the traffic started getting busy with rush hour. Stephanie and I raced to our respective kids' activities to pick them up and get their dinners on the table and oversee homework and dogs and dishes. Stephanie coined this the SSS—the suburban shit shuffle—the frenetic driving around to kids' activities that happens every afternoon from the last bell at school to lights-out in just about every suburban home in the country. I felt fine that afternoon and was up to the challenge. In fact, I felt fine for two or three days before I started getting a little woozy. It was not bad though, that first round. I napped every day but was pretty functional overall.

Round two was three weeks later, and my parents were back to help out. Same scenario: got my bracelet, got my blood drawn, got my body stats taken. My blood pressure was 164/101—a little high. The nurse had me sit and relax and took it three times. During my frenzied and tooth-filled checkup with Dr. Carrey, he suggested I should start taking some medication to lower it. Dr. Carrey then went over all my bloodwork, keeping an especially close eye on any signs my kidneys were struggling. Everything looked fine. I left and went to get strapped in by Susie to my infusion bags.

Stephanie didn't trust that my parents would gather the patience to sit through the hours of infusion time with me. It is a lot of sitting around, and my parents are an active duo. Stephanie showed up, bag of treats and magazines in hand, ready to take her place as my chemo caregiver, her presence a sine qua non to my recovery. I felt well taken care of as a little power struggle ensued; Stephanie told my parents she would be happy to keep me company if they would like to go out to lunch or into the city to shop or home to rest. My parents said they were perfectly happy to stay and keep me company, and all three sat with me awhile before Stephanie headed home to get a start on the SSS, asking me to let her know if I felt she should return at any point.

As with round one, the first few days were fine; a little tougher, but I was relieved I was getting through without too many issues. I even made a hair appointment. I love getting my hair washed—it is hands-down the best part of the salon experience. The day before the hair appointment, my hair started coming out in clumps—big clumps. I will go over hair stuff in the next chapter, but when mine started to go, it went fast. It took about four days before just a few strands were left, and I decided to go ahead and just shave them off.

I had been given the name and number of the head nurse at the thoracic department and told to call with any concerns or questions between rounds. I called after round two about two things. The first was that my period had stopped. She said that happens all the time. Chemotherapy often brings on menopause; not to worry. Phew! And what a silver lining! I was pleased to receive the gift of that particular switch turned off. (I ended up calling her again a few months later to say I had bleeding that was similar to having my period, and I was concerned about some internal damage going on. She then told me it was also completely normal for a period to start up again after chemotherapy was done. Bummer.)

The second issue I asked her about was my hair falling out. She told me that was not possible. My chemotherapy did not cause hair loss. I looked like a Minion. I sported huge chunks of baldness on my head. It actually is possible.

Almost everything else was self-explanatory to me. I was just working my way through the chemotherapy step. Time and patience.

Stephanie copiloted once again during round three, three weeks after round two, and I felt as though we were hitting our stride. It was getting routine. I did bring in flowers from my garden and some cookies for the nursing staff this round. What a great group nurses are. It is impossible to appreciate them enough. They remind me of teachers—so important and so capable of shaping experiences.

My fourth and final round was faster than the three-week interval. Dr. Carrey was a little concerned about pushing me so much. "Are you positive you want to do the fourth round today?" he asked as he reviewed my bloodwork numbers on the computer screen in his examining room. "It's a little fast. You might want to wait a week or two. Or maybe even settle for three rounds."

"My kids get out of school in two weeks, and my older daughter is turning thirteen next Wednesday. I want to be done and on with the recovery for when they are home. I don't want to be going through the first ten days of post-infusion while they are on vacation; it's nice to rest during the school day."

I did think about the invitation to stop at round three. Many people I communicated with only did three rounds. But the thing is, I didn't know how much was going to be enough. I decided to go for round four, so as not to leave anything on the table. I wanted to know I did everything I possibly could to ensure I would not experience a recurrence. I sure didn't want to ever go through this again.

"Well, your numbers are pretty good. And we did say we wanted to go at this as aggressively as possible. And this is definitely aggressive. So, if you feel up to it—let's go!" With a dazzling display of dental encouragement, he departed to dispatch my session.

My parents were visiting again for round four and hung out with me during the daylong process of bloodwork, doctors' appointments, and infusions. This is where the threshold of unbearable and unendurable met for me. I fell asleep during the fourth round; I am unclear if it was my body just needing the rest or if the round was just too much, too soon. It felt like too much that week. It was the hardest week for me during recovery, and I lingered just within the bounds of functioning. Chemotherapy is somewhat cumulative, as the body can't rid all the toxins out completely between rounds. It took almost a month for me to feel more human than zombie. Fortunately it was June, and the weather was beautiful; fresh air seemed to help a lot. Just being outside with the sun shining is an elixir for many things.

Maggie became a teenager Wednesday, and we threw her a surprise party a few days before the actual date, on Saturday. Twelve friends met in our barn, while the thirteenth took Maggie shopping and brought her back to be surprised. I wanted Maggie to enjoy the party, to be the birthday girl, to create the memory. I wanted her to relish a reprieve—to wallow in a moment of carefree kid time. I felt there had been a role reversal of late, with Maggie and Jane asking me if they could bring me something and helping out around the house as I rested. My role of Mom felt somewhat diminished. I had planned and executed birthday parties since Maggie turned four, fabulous birthday parties with outrageous themes. All were hosted at home. I didn't want to falter now.

I stayed awake for the party—and that was about all I could muster two days after that fourth round. I wore my "good" wig, and it was hot and itchy. I tried to be up to chat with the other moms, who all wanted to learn how everything was going. Most, thankfully, didn't stay long, and many remarked about how tired I appeared. (Which we all know is a euphemism for "you look like shit." And I did, and I knew it. What can you do?)

Stephanie came by with her husband, Bob, and two younger daughters. She'd recently had a bunion removed and was on crutches. Other friends were visiting from Maine with their two girls and herded their daughters and mine to a movie right after the party. My parents cleaned up, and I zonked out on the couch. The festivity was at the outer limits of what I could manage, and I am thrilled to have been able to pull it all together for Maggie. I am hopeful her memory of becoming a teenager will be about the surprise and her friends and not the cancer and the chemotherapy.

There's something very comforting about having the chemotherapy step done. I was very anxious to get my scan and to determine no other tumors had developed since the surgery. My last scan had been in March, and my first scan post chemotherapy was August 9. That is a long time to worry. There are a lot of aches and pains that come from being middle aged and from chemotherapy, and it is very hard not to think each and every one of them is a tumor pressing on some vital organ. Headaches are what get me. They haunt my worry about a tumor in my brain. I suffer headaches all the time. Dr. TG said he would be concerned if I didn't experience stress headaches, given the amount of worry I carry around. He offered to prescribe a brain scan, but I was concerned about the amount of radiation my body had received. I think we all learn to live with some uncertainty—a small silvery thorn in our shoe as we take each day as it comes, one step at a time.

Tips for Chemotherapy

1) *Be prepared.* Have a contact at the hospital to ask questions to in the event your doctor is not available.

   Stock up on bland foods and energy drinks. Keep some plastic utensils around.
   I bought an extra covering for my bathtub drain, so my hair wouldn't clog my pipes if it started to fall out.
   Be mindful that your skin will be super sensitive with chemo; stay out of the sun as much as possible. Set up a nice chaise in the shade, and wear sunscreen.

2) *Get help.* If you can work it into your budget, arrange to have your house cleaned regularly. See about getting some extra help for yard or snow or everything. If you are able to hire help or give tasks away, do it. Better yet, get someone else to organize and dole out your household responsibilities if possible. You will inevitably have a good deal of chores and errands and responsibilities to keep you feeling needed and helpful and involved—if you want to be. This may be the first time in your adult life you are given a free pass to be entirely selfish. You have been dealt a never-ending deck of cancer cards to play out as you see fit. A friend of mine told me to use mine indiscriminately and often but to stop once done with recovering from chemotherapy. I thought this was good advice and doled out mine every which way during treatment.

3) *Exercise.* Ugh. And important. I discovered and found I love hot yoga. Yoga is now up there with massage for me. Hot yoga sounds a little like yoga for menopausal women, but is yoga in a sauna-type room. I loved imagining the toxins from my chemotherapy exuding out with all that sweat. Besides, you get to wear exercise clothes and sweat without having to move much. I felt totally athletic.

4) *Find a veteran mentor.* I was given the remarkable gift of being introduced to a lung cancer survivor who at the time of my diagnosis

was celebrating five years disease free. I called her about a month into treatment, and we discussed issues and insights and concerns. She had been diagnosed with lung cancer the day after running the Boston Marathon. We were both diagnosed in our mid-forties, neither of us smoke, we both were moms to school-aged kids, and we live in the same smallish town. These veterans know the fight; brandish the scars, the insights, the experiences; and have emerged victorious. If they can do it, so can you.

5) *Get support.* This is different from help. Help is for the things in life; support is for the *life* in life. Along with a mentor, find a therapist and a support group. You are going through a lot. You need a place to unload, to share, to vent. It frees up family and friends trying their best to absorb what they might not be able to.

6) *Find an easy way to keep everyone up to date with your progress.* Keep up with your blog or group e-mails or whatever system you choose. Find a good way that works for you to continue to keep people in the loop— this will not only ease people's minds but also alleviate answering a lot of individual e-mails and texts. It will be a good way for you to read back over all the great progress you've made. Caringbridge.org is an excellent, free online resource.

7) *Hair.* If you are convinced you will lose your hair, and it's long enough, consider proactively donating before it starts to fall out. I wish I had cut and given mine to a charity; it would have made losing it worth something.

8) *Be social.* This was hard for me. I went to lunch at least weekly and would go to yoga five times a week as soon as I was done with treatment. I ran into people I knew at the yoga studio, so I felt connected. I walked with a neighbor a few times a week. This journey can be isolating. Try to stay involved with your friends and family.

9) *Maintain a healthy weight.* It was a cruel twist that my regimen made me gain weight. The concern, though, is too much weight loss; a loss

of appetite is very common. Eat frequent small meals. Again, it's a balancing act.

10) *Work out a schedule at work.* We all have bills to pay, and most of us need to work in order to pay them. Check with your insurance about short-term disability or other benefits you may have available to help. I will put some references in the back of the book for some organizations that might be able to give assistance if you end up having needs that can't easily be met.

11) *Organize your calendar.* If you don't know how to use the handy calendar or appointment app on your phone, find a teen to help you figure it out. Chemo brain is coming, and that little calendar can be mighty handy. I would forget during my day at Dana Farber which appointment was next, what floor it was on, or which doctor I was supposed to be meeting. All I needed was to check and recheck my phone to keep on track. When you leave the hospital, you will schedule multiple appointments for your next round. Put these in right away, as the printout they hand you may get misplaced.

12) *Do something for yourself every week.* Go in for a massage or a facial or to the movies, or simply carve out an hour to read in the hammock or nap. Avoid manicures and pedicures, as you need to steer clear of any chance of infection, and nail salons are notorious as hotbeds for bacteria and fungus. Wait until after chemo treatments for this splurge. Choose something that feels pampering. You deserve it.

Tips for the Team

1) *Offer to go to chemotherapy and doctors' appointments.* Chemotherapy is a pretty big time commitment, and it may be that your friend's significant other may not have the flexibility to attend all the dates. It's nice to pass the time with good company. Bring a book, a deck of cards, healthy snacks, and some magazines. Of course, avoid any contact if you are sick or under the weather at all. Chemo does a number on the immune system, and having to battle the flu or anything else on top of it would be a struggle.

2) *Have meals and errands handled as needed.* This is a nice and appreciated gift. Same with all household help, including shoveling or mowing or taking the trash out or walking the dog.

3) *Give a gift certificate for a massage.* Maybe there are a few on the planet who don't like a massage, but for those of us who do, this is a great gift.

4) *Give little pick-me-ups.* I loved the little gift left on the table outside our front door. It cheered me to know people were thinking of me and they understood I may not be up for a visit, but I would appreciate that they stopped by.

5) *Continue to e-mail or text funny videos or jokes.* Put a funny card in the mail, and keep sending the amusing e-mails and videos. They are great distractions.

6) *Offer to go for a walk with her.* Good company and a little exercise on a nice day are perfect.

7) *Check in with the kids.* Invite them to dinner, the movies, sleepovers, or ice cream. Sometimes life makes you grow up early. Childhood can't be put on hold. There are no second chances to be a kid.

8) *Take care of yourself.* If you are a member of the support team, don't forget you need some extra TLC also. Eat well and drink plenty of

water. This is a lot for you too. Unloading on a therapist might be a good idea.

9) *Gift basket ideas*—Ginger has been shown to help soothe upset stomachs. Bring a gift basket with ginger snaps, ginger tea, ginger ale, and maybe a video of the most favorite ginger of all: Lucille Ball. If she is going to or has lost her hair, put together some nice scarves, baseball caps from her favorite team, and a few sun hats or warm caps. As a group gift, friends or coworkers could go in on a chaise or hammock, a few pillows, and a good book.

10) *Respect her decision.* This is hard. She may make a decision about treatment that you don't agree with. You need to put your opinions aside and respect that she knows herself better than anyone and that whatever decision she made was thoughtful and the right one for her.

11) *Pray.*

Hair

A woman who cuts her hair is about to change her life.
—Coco Chanel

The second question Jane asked me when I sat her down that snowy Sunday back in February was if I was going to lose my hair. At that time I had no idea. It's curious to me an eleven-year-old had it ingrained socially to worry about having a bald mom. I didn't know what it would feel like to be bald. The ability to grocery shop and pick up kids from school and go to the drugstore incognito as a healthy person is taken away. Because you don't necessarily appear sick when you have hair and are walking the aisles and can be easily mistaken for "normal." Baldness proclaims *cancer* in women, and people assume all sorts of things when confronted with a bald woman. A wide range of emotions from fear to compassion washes over faces before they quickly glance away. Take a look around you at the mall or grocery store or school sometime. It's astounding to think of how many of us are just trying to look "normal."

Hair is a funny thing. In my lifetime it's become acceptable to be a bald guy. The recent plethora of hot bald men, led by Michael Jordan, made being male and bald sexy and fashionable. When I was in my twenties, my boyfriend spent his hard-earned money on hair plugs. Now men are bold when bald, and it is accepted. People don't question if a man is ill or going through chemotherapy when he steps out with a shiny dome. Hair, for women, is different. In the Bible, loss of hair is considered a punishment for women. In the Old Testament, in Isaiah 3:16, the Lord announces the women of Zion are "haughty, walking along with outstretched necks, flirting with their eyes, strutting along with swaying hips, with ornaments jingling on their ankles." To punish this display of vanity, the Lord "made their scalps bald"; "instead of well-dressed hair, baldness; instead of fine clothing, sackcloth; instead of beauty, branding." But where is it written a woman's beauty or worth or merit is determined by the length of her hair?

Another story in the Bible about hair loss involves Elisha, a bald guy, who walked up to Bethel one day, and a group of kids started mocking him for his baldness, yelling, "Go on up, you baldhead!" Elisha turned around and cursed them in the name of the Lord, and two bears burst out of the woods and mauled forty-two of those kids. Now I question the justice of forty-two kids being mauled for calling out a bald guy. I have trouble understanding quite a few things about God and righteousness. Like why potato chips and bacon were created to taste so good and are so bad for you, or why mosquitoes or Ebola exist. Or AIDS. Or cancer.

I didn't worry about losing my hair. I know a lot of women do. I was more worried about getting the large tumor out of my lung and holding on to my life than whether or not I held on to a full head of hair. And then it started falling out. It fell out fast and furious after my second round of chemotherapy. I wore a baseball cap for a few days, but once I began to resemble Gollum, I figured the best way to move forward was to start fresh.

Here's how the call to the Dana Farber nurse went:

"My hair is falling out. Quite a bit of it."

"No, your hair shouldn't fall out with the chemotherapy treatment you are getting."

"Ummm, well, it *is* falling out. I've got some quite big bald patches."

"It's not supposed to."

"Okay. Well, I'm not sure what to say … maybe it might make sense to mention there is a slim chance of it happening, since apparently it *is* possible. Some patients may want to be prepared."

"Well, it's not supposed to fall out."

"Oh, okay. Well, thank you."

I found a few times that the symptoms I had were dismissed by the medical team if they didn't match what the books were saying I ought to be experiencing. This is when being in touch with others going through the same course of chemotherapy helped me most. These survivors are not those inclined to rely solely on studies and science and what *should* be happening; these are compatriots in vomit and blood and scars and tears and participants in what is happening out in the real world. I learned through them that although nearly everyone treated with Cis-flatten kept her hair, some others had been compelled to place the few strands left on their dome under the razor and pick out a wig just like I did.

My brother Mark was visiting again, and we picked up Maggie and Jane from middle school at lunch one day and drove into Boston.

"This is going to be terrific. I can't wait to kiss your bald head," Mark announced on the way.

"Excuse me?"

"Well, when was the last time anyone kissed your bald head?"

"Ummm, probably around birth."

"That's right! And I get to do it now, and likely no one will ever do it again. This is going to be great!"

A few years ago, both of the girls cut off their ponytails and donated them to the Pantene charity, Beautiful Lengths. Maggie had eight inches to give of her wild, curly, thick hair, and I cut off over a foot of Jane's fine, blonde, straight hair. I assumed I would want a natural-hair wig, since it would appear, well, natural. I'm glad in retrospect Dana Farber doesn't offer them. I was surprised wigs made from natural hair were not available there. I wonder where the wigs made from all those donated ponytails go if one of the biggest cancer centers in the country doesn't have any at all.

I learned that real-hair wigs are higher maintenance and need to be styled every day. I rarely style my hair—especially since having kids. I am a wash-and-go gal. And I certainly did not want to add anything to my plate at this point. Natural-hair wigs are the most expensive, and I was shopping with my prescription for hair and my $350 insurance allowance for my prosthetic part. (Free wigs are available through the American Cancer Society and CancerCare. Check out the resources at the end of the book.)

Dana Farber has a beauty parlor and shaves heads for free. It struck me that the barber chair faces a blank wall; there are no mirrors. I guess no one wants to see herself shorn. I didn't mind it much. When it came time, the stylist asked if it was okay if the girls or my brother wanted to stay. Mark said he would wait in the shop outside the salon area, but both Jane and Maggie wanted to be included as the remnants of my hair were cropped. They stood by giggling and making snide comments throughout, which was a great distraction to the buzz of the razor and the quickly growing small pile of my hair, newly colored with auburn highlights from my recent salon visit. And as soon as the kind woman finished, Mark gave the top of my head a big kiss. True to his word.

I tried on a variety of wigs in an assortment of styles before choosing one similar to my usual hairstyle (except much more refined and "done") and one with a little bob showing under a baseball cap. This one I liked and wore quite a bit. Maggie and Jane had fun picking out different looks and colors for me. I know it is devastating for some women. Maybe it will become fashionable for women to be bald someday. I do know I immediately felt marked being bald. When people popped in unannounced, I had to look for my "hair" to open the door. Or if they stopped by while I was out back in the yard without my wig, I would suffer the pitying looks mixed with their embarrassment of finding me standing around bald. There is an immediate change in perception. Where once I could be overlooked and treated like everyone else, I was now conspicuously sick. And I looked different to myself, which took some getting used to.

So my all-synthetic wig was fine; the lady even trimmed the bangs a bit, and I was good to go. The biggest benefit is that it is totally low maintenance. I am a little embarrassed to say other than a quick swipe with a brush here and there, I did practically nothing for or to that wig. Wigs usually only last a couple of months, but most people grow hair back by then. I know some get two wigs, especially if they go with the higher-maintenance varieties—one to wear, the other dropped off to be styled. Some choose a more formal one for workdays and a more casual one for weekends. Have fun with it. Look at all those celebrities sporting wigs; join the cutting-edge celebs.

Here is your chance to never have a bad hair day.

I was given a little skullcap to wear under my wig, to help with the scratchiness. It was summer, and I preferred wearing scarves because they are lighter and colorful and feel nice, but silk will easily fall off, and those little caps are indispensible in keeping them in place. I bought some scarves at Dana Farber already tied like a pirate's cap that are fast and easy. I felt an affinity to other women I saw with scarves or out baring their baldness. It reminded me of the kinship appreciated when in a foreign country and hearing English spoken, or one Star-Bellied Sneetch discovering another—total tribal pride.

After a few months, I ended up packing the wig stand and special shampoo and hats and scarves—some still with the price tags on them—and giving them all to a friend of a friend who had just been diagnosed. It turns out that summer I preferred to go au naturel most of the time.

When my hair started growing back about six weeks later, it was white, soft, and fuzzy like a Q-tip. Then it morphed into my natural hair color, although thicker, and as curly as a fusilli noodle. I had had the same style of long, straight hair ever since my high school perm faded, but now I plan on keeping it short for a while. Thank goodness for Anne Hathaway and how fabulous she looked with her short, short hair after *Les Miserables*. I went out about four months post shear and felt cutting-edge chic with my crew cut. I am fairly confident I still appeared as though I was growing out the stubble, but if I squinted at myself just right in the mirror, I could totally see a cutting edge fashion statement. It's part of the new me.

I will say it was weird for me to lose my eyelashes and eyebrows. I hadn't anticipated losing them, and it changed my features quite a bit. I realize I sound a little naive, but clearly hair had not been a focus of mine. I was so fixated on getting through the surgery and then chemotherapy, I didn't pause to consider the collateral damage of body hair. Now some people will go out and get the press-on eyelashes and draw in eyebrows; I couldn't be bothered. I just waited for them to return, and they did a few months later.

Being bald has its benefits. It cooled the summer, and the stubbly softness was mesmerizing to rub. It felt like the small, soft bristles of a loved teddy bear. I often see men who absently rub their bare heads, and I get it now; it's like the belly of the Buddha or a rabbit's foot or a smooth worry stone. It feels good and seems like it should bring you luck. It can be a bit obsessive. I saved a bunch on shampoo and conditioner and had no need to dry or brush or style. Easy as pie. And by the way, do you realize chemotherapy includes *all* of your body hair? No waxing or shaving or tweezing for the duration. There's another silver lining.

Tips for Hair

1) *It's only hair.* It will grow back.

2) *Try new styles when choosing a wig* or new colors. Here is your chance to get the hairdo you never dared to try before. If you think you will want something similar to what you have going on now, take pictures of your hair—front, sides, and back—to take in with you when getting a wig. If you know you are going to lose it, go in before chemotherapy and line a wig up. This may be a good time to consider donating your locks.

3) *Invest in some hats and scarves.* There are many to choose from. Stephanie and I went to the store at Dana Farber, and I tried on at least fifty different hat and scarf combinations. It can be a fun outing. Include in your purchases the handy-dandy skullcap, which is instrumental in keeping the scarves in place.

4) *Buy a swim cap.* If you will be without hair and plan on being at the beach or a pool and doing some swimming, your wig will not want to go in with you.

5) *Keep a cap by the door.* Our doorbell would ring, and I would be looking around for a hat or wig to put on before answering it. Leave a baseball cap or something right next to the door, so you can slip it on whenever you need to.

6) *Check with your insurance.* You may be eligible for an allowance to spend toward wigs. I spent pretty much the full $350 on the two wigs I bought. The nicer wig was almost $300 and the little cap wig, which I actually preferred, was about $50.

7) *Make an appointment.* Unless you want a friend to shave your head, you will need an appointment. My hairdresser offered to keep the salon open late or come in early to shear my head in private. It might

be awkward to be at a salon filled with the ladies while your head is being shaved. Dana Farber needed an appointment, and not a lot was available when I called. So consider calling at the first signs of hair loss, to get on the books. Or do the backyard salon—glass of wine, some music, a few good friends. Whatever you want.

8) *Wash your scalp.* Even though you no longer have hair, it is still important to shampoo your scalp every couple of days. Without hair, your scalp can get dirty, oily, or dry out. There is an array of products for the unhirsute, most of which can be found at the local drugstore.

9) *Sunscreen.* If you will be out au naturel with your clean scalp, remember to put sunscreen on your head. Choose a brand geared toward bald heads, so you don't risk lotion running into your eyes.

10) *Cold cap treatment.* A newish treatment is available that is basically a freezing-cold, big blue diaper-type cap designed to keep your hair from falling out during chemotherapy. Apparently it is painful, expensive, and effective. Talk with your oncologist or check it out online if you are nervous about losing your hair.

11) *Give it time.* It does grow back.

Tips for the Team

1) *Do not drop by unannounced.* It was awkward to receive unexpected company, especially when I got comfortable walking around the house and yard without my wig or a hat. It was summer and hot, and the girls got used to my new 'do. It was a bit embarrassing for all of us whenever company showed up by surprise. It only takes a minute to text or call first.

2) *Be okay with it.* This is hard to articulate. We hosted quite a bit of company, some overnight, while I was going through chemo and my hair was growing back. Out of respect for how our guests might feel seeing me bald, I would start out by wearing my wig or a hat. It was in the eighties and summer. I was uncomfortably hot and itchy. Every one of our guests suggested early on for me to take off my wig or hat and then did not react, which made me feel so grateful. In a short time, I forgot I was bald, as the conversation kept up and I was not given any weird glances. We would just go on as we normally would. That was all I wanted, to get to normal.

3) *Ask if she wants company to go to clip her hair.* Or offer to cut off the ponytail for donation. Or shave her head. Many do their own shearing right out on the back deck.

Wrapping It Up

And once the storm is over you won't remember how you made it through … you won't be the same person who walked in. That's what the storm's all about.

—Haruki Murakami

Live your life with arms wide open
Today is where your book begins
The rest is still unwritten

—Natasha Bedingfield

I don't know if I believe in God or not, but lately I'm spending a lot more time praying and God-bartering, which seems to be working out okay, since I'm still around.

I don't go to church, but I do send up prayers to both a Goddess and a God as I go about Life. I pray to my Goddess when I want to make certain she knows how thankful I am for my girls and for my health, family, and friends. I figure a nurturing God must be an omnipresent Mother who wants to be kept up to date on her kids' trials and triumphs and tribulations. Of course I also pray to her for guidance in raising my girls and for continued good health and patience and wisdom and just the right amount of wine to bring them up without losing what remains of my sanity.

I imagine my Goddess wears white, diaphanous layers and is voluptuous with nice skin and a good haircut and a french manicure. She has a few extra pounds to provide the ultimate comfort level for hugs and reassurances and nonjudgment. She is a Southern Baptist Goddess with a soulful voice, and she is strong—a no-nonsense presence with an overabundance of ever-lovin' kindness.

I am thankful every single day. I find something: a good cup of coffee in the morning, toilet paper on the roll—thank you! A green light—thank you! A sunny day, a paid bill, the sound of my daughters laughing, a full tank of gas, a rainy day—thank you! Thank you! Thank you! I say thank you all day long, so I won't sound like such a whiner or ungrateful or completely self-absorbed when I ask for a little something. I don't want her to think I'm taking anything for granted. I truly try to live that way, and I sometimes succeed. I don't have the strength needed to meet or overcome some of the struggles Life slings out, and sometimes I want her to simply hold me in her hand and keep me from falling while I rest up a bit.

I pray to my Father God when I want justice or strength or solutions. I let him know I'm thankful for plenty, but mostly it's a clenched-teeth type of praying when I'm angry or upset or just tying the knot at the end of my rope and asking for extra help to hold on until tomorrow. I want him to be my vengeful, wrathful, and righteous God and to smite people down for me. Just a little smiting like Siberian exile or solitary confinement or poison-ivy outbreaks on private parts. Usually nothing too permanent or drastic. Usually.

I know they both have a lot going on in the world, and there are many requiring time and consideration and guidance much greater than mine. I just like the idea I may have *two* supreme beings watching out for me—in case one is justifiably otherwise occupied.

I know it's become somewhat trendy to go around eating and laughing and praying and loving all day long. My experience is that life can be a bit more of a shit storm, and even if I was granted the "gift" to go through life that way, I'm not sure I would choose it. It seems a bit of a flat line. A lot of interesting stuff happens when you roll your pants up and wade into some of Life's murkier waters. It's often the things that go wrong that make the memories, give the screen a little "blip." Think back on all the weddings you've been to—the mishaps make them memorable and give them life. I in *no* way want you to think I consider cancer as a mishap. I just want to suggest this is part of the journey, and looking back, you will discover you met people who inspired and touched you, you rediscovered your fantastic family and friends, you got a life reminder card attached to the cancer card—a stark revealing of the fragility of life.

So use your cancer cards indiscriminately. And when you are done with this part of the journey, reach out a hand to those at the base of the mountain. Help them with rolling the rock up. Let's see how crowded we can get it here at the summit, and help as many as we can to join us for the view.

One day at a time. One step at a time.

Breathe in, breathe out. Repeat.

Acknowledgments

I have so many people to thank who made it possible for me to be here and write this. I am beholden to the neighbors, friends, fellow patients, and family who helped and supported me throughout my treatment and the compiling of this book. My aunts, uncles, and cousins, showered me with support and provided me a broad platform from which to heal. My Gramma Van is a never-ending source of insights and inspiration.

I am unbelievably grateful to the dedication and expertise of the medical staff at Brigham and Women's, Dana Farber and Mass General Hospital. I quite literally owe my life to them.

Marti, Linda, Diana, Julie, Laurie, Juliana, Mike, Spud, Dianne, and my parents all read my rough drafts and offered such encouragement and great feedback – I'm not sure I would have ever finished without you all.

I have to especially thank my parents, Jack and Nancy, my sister, Jill, and brother, Mark, for standing by and walking with me through the entire cancer route, so I had someone standing by at all times. When they were unavailable, Stephanie was never far away with a willingness and grace that is utterly astonishing.

My extraordinary daughters, Ryan and CJ, are my strength, my determination, and my inspiration to get me through everything.

Resources

Here are just some of the excellent resources for free information and assistance.

Air Charity Network
www.Aircharitynetwork.org
877-621-7177

Free air transportation to specialized healthcare facilities to qualifying patients.

American Cancer Society
www.cancer.org
800-227-2345

They are available to you twenty-four hours a day, seven days a week.

This society is all-encompassing, and the site is excellent. You can find out all sorts of information about the Family and Medical Leave Act, the Americans with Disabilities Act, what to do if you are uninsured, how to handle medical claim denials, people and places to help and support you, etc. They also have patient-resource navigators who will work with you and give you advice on just about every conceivable topic. It's very good place to start.

American Lung Association
www.lung.org
800-LUNG-USA

This group targets women in particular and focuses on not only lung cancer but also lung health.

Angel Wheels to Healing
www.Angelwheels.org

This nonprofit organization provides financially disadvantaged patients with primarily long-distance ground transportation (up to three hundred miles) for nonemergency medical situations. They will also help to offset gas expenses or any commercial ground transportation such as bus and train tickets.

Association of Cancer Online Resources
www.acor.org

This organization provides a plethora of online resources where anyone can discuss all things medically related.

BenefitsCheckUp
www.Benefitscheckup.org
800-677-1116

This free service is run by the National Council on Aging and helps support patients over fifty-five with medical and other needs. These folks will help you find federal, state, and private programs that are specifically designed to save you money and cover both medical as well as everyday expenses—food, utilities, taxes, transportation, etc.

Cancer and Careers
www.cancerandcareers.org

Cancer and Careers will help with issues that cancer patients are confronted by in the workplace.

CancerCare
www.cancercare.org
800-813-HOPE (4673)

CancerCare provides free education, counseling, and practical help by professional oncology social workers. There is also some financial assistance available for such things as childcare, medication, transportation, and home care.

CancerCare Copayment Assistance Foundation
www.cancercarecopay.org
212-601-9750
(An offshoot of CancerCare.)

This is the financial-assistance arm of CancerCare.

Cancer Financial Coalition Foundation (CFAC)
www.cancerfac.org

This can be a very helpful site for those struggling with paying for treatment. This organization combines fourteen different agencies and is all about helping you pay for any and all expenses related to your treatment. After you input your ZIP code, they have a drop-down menu where you can search for resources in your area that help with medical expenses, drugs, housing, prosthetics, children—the whole gamut. One thing to bear in mind here is that they do not respond to individual requests; they are here to help point you to organizations designed to help you in your area.

Cancer.Net
www.cancer.net
888-651-3038

This site is run by the 35,000 members of the American Society of Clinical Oncologists and gives excellent information to make more informed decisions about cancer care.

The Cancer Support Community
www.cancersupportcommunity.org
888-793-9355

This is a global nonprofit network of psychosocial oncology mental-health professionals, providing support and education to cancer patients, their families, and caregivers.

The Chain Fund
www.thechainfund.com

This fund specifically assists the financial needs of cancer patients. The needs covered include rent, utilities, mortgage, insurance, etc. They also have some workshops available.

Cleaning for a Reason
www.cleaningforareason.org
877-337-3348

Cleaning for a Reason partners with maid services to have cleaners come and clean your house—for free—while you are going through treatment.

Conquer Cancer Foundation
www.conquercancerfoundation.org
571-483-1700

Corporate Angel Network
www.corporateangelnetwork.org
914-328-1313

This group uses empty seats on corporate jets to help cancer patients travel free of charge to the best possible treatment centers anywhere in the United States.

**Friends Are by Your Side
(Wigs and Wishes)**
www.friendsarebyyourside.com
856-582-6600

These folks have paired up with salons around the world to provide free wigs to women who have lost their hair to chemotherapy.

GiveForward
www.giveforward.com

GiveForward is a platform to fundraise for medical expenses online.

The Healthcare Hospitality Network
www.hhnetwork.org
800-542-9730

This network is a pool of nonprofit lodging and support services for patients and their families who may need to travel far from home for treatment.

Joe's House
www.joeshouse.org
877-563-7468

Joe's House gives you a listing of different hotels or lodging that are near major cancer centers in the country.

The LiveStrong Foundation
www.livestrong.org
877-236-8820 (LIVESTRONG)

Lung Cancer Alliance Group
www.lungcanceralliance.org
800-298-2436

These people do it all.

National Comprehensive Cancer Network
www.nccn.org
215-690-0300

I received the NCCN publication with information regarding cancer guidelines and staging and found it to be extraordinarily useful. This is another invaluable resource.

The National Cancer Institute
www.cancer.gov
800-4-CANCER (This about sums it up. It is an all-inclusive cancer site.)

The National Patient Travel Center
www.patienttravel.org
800-296-1217

These guys will help you find the best possible transportation to where you need to be for treatment with "maximum efficiency and minimal cost."

Needy Meds
www.needymeds.org
800-503-6897

Needy Meds provides you with financial resources to help you afford your medications.

The Partnership for Prescription Assistance
www.pparx.org

The Patient Advocate Foundation
www.patientadvocate.org
800-532-5274

This foundation provides one-on-one assistance with managing your healthcare needs and any issues that might arise.

The Patrick Dempsey Center for Cancer Hope & Healing

www.dempseycenter.org

877-336-8287

This center is based in Lewiston, Maine, and I've heard great things about it. If you are in the area, check it out.

The Social Security Disability Resource Center

www.ssdrc.com

This site walks you through what you need to do to file a Social Security disability claim.

Terminology

There's a language to cancer and cancer treatment. Here are some of the common terms I learned along the way. (This is far from complete.)

The National Cancer Institute, www.cancer.net, is a great resource for terminology.

alopecia—loss of hair

anaphylaxis—a severe allergic reaction; symptoms include shortness of breath, rash, wheezing, and a drop in blood pressure

antiemetic—antinausea drug

benign—not cancerous

biomarkers—genes, proteins, and other biologic molecules that predict the behavior of cancer; also called markers

bone scan—a nuclear scanning test to find certain abnormalities in bone such as cancer, fractures, infection, or any other cause that is damaging the bone

Ca-125—blood-test marker for some types of cancer

cancer remission—a period of time when the cancer is responding to treatment or is under control *chemo* and *chemotx*—chemotherapy

CINV—chemo-induced nausea and vomiting

CIPN—chemo-induced peripheral neuropathy

complete cancer remission—all the signs and symptoms of the disease have disappeared; complete cancer remissions may continue for several years and be considered cured

CT or *CAT scan*—computerized axial tomography; creates a 3-D picture of organs and tissues

DEXA scan or *DXA*—a low-exposure x-ray test measuring bone density

Dx—diagnosis

DFS—disease-free survival

DNA—deoxyribonucleic acid; the molecules inside cells that carry genetic information passed from parent to child

edema—swelling caused by the abnormal accumulation of fluid in body tissues

gene—the basic functional and physical unit of heredity that is passed on from parent to child

gene profiling—the technique to identify genes that are turned on or off in a specific tumor to help plan the best treatment for a patient and/or predict response to treatment

genetics—the study of how genes are passed from parent to child

GI—gastrointestinal

HDC—high-dose chemotherapy

IP—intraperitoneal (the area that contains the abdominal organs)

IV—intravenous

IVP—intravenous push

LUL—left upper lobe

lymphedema—extra lymph fluid builds up, causing tissues to swell in legs and arms; may occur if lymph vessels are damaged, blocked, or removed by surgery

malignancy, malignant neoplasm, and *malignant tumor*—cancer

markers—see *biomarkers*

mass—tumor (also called lesions or nodules)

metastatic/metastasis—cancer that has spread to another part of the body

MRI—magnetic resonance imaging. Radio waves and a powerful magnet linked to a computer are used to create detailed pictures of areas inside the body. These pictures can show the difference between normal and diseased tissue. MRI is especially useful for imaging the brain, the spine, the soft tissue of joints, and the inside of bones.

MRT—magnetic resonance tomography; see *MRI*

NMRI—nuclear magnetic resonance imaging; see *MRI*

NED—no evidence of disease; people often say they are "dancing with Ned"

NMR—nuclear magnetic resonance; see *MRI*

OS—overall survival

PR—partial response

persistent disease—cancer still remains after treatment

PET—positron emission tomography (scan); a small amount of radioactive glucose is injected into a vein, and this scan will show which parts of the body are using up the most of it; cancer cells love glucose

pleura—the thin layers of tissue lining the lung and the wall of the chest cavity

pleural effusion—an excess of fluid that accumulates in the pleura; excessive amounts of such fluid can impair breathing by limiting the expansion of the lungs

premedications—drugs given prior to chemotherapy to prevent nausea or allergic reactions

PFS—progression-free survival; a patient is living with cancer, but it's not getting any worse

PO—oral

recurrence—cancer has returned after treatment

SC/SQ—subcutaneous

SD—stable disease

SOB—shortness of breath

stage—describes where the cancer is located, where it may have spread, and if it's affecting other parts of the body; there are five stages for cancer: zero through four *targeted therapy*—a treatment designed to block a specific gene or protein that has a critical role in the survival, growth, invasion, or metastasis of a specific cancer cell

VEGF-AS—a humanized monoclonal antibody that is being studied in the treatment of cancer; it recognizes and blocks vascular endothelial growth factor (VEGF-A), which is needed for angiogenesis—the development of new blood vessels that carry nutrients to a tumor

Citations

Chapter 2

Quote: "It's far more important to know what person the disease has than what disease the person has." Hippocrates. (n.d.) BrainyQuote.com. Xplore Inc, 2015. http://www.brainyquote.com/quotes/authors/hippocrates.html, accessed October 8, 2015.

"It partners with melancholy to make up the first of Galen's four humors." Galen's four humors: US National Library of Medicine—History of Medicine, published 1846.

"This ancient scroll tells of eight tumors or cysts cauterized from breasts by a 'fire drill.'" Edwin Smith Papyrus—*Discover* magazine by Carl Engel King. March 18, 2014. "Oldest Case of Cancer Discovered in Ancient Skeleton".

"Celsus, a first-century Roman, wrote a series of encyclopedias with topics ranging from agriculture to philosophy and medicine." Celsus books- DeMedicina, published 1478. https://wikipedia.org/wiki/aulus_cornelius_celsus

"The term cancer originates from the Grand Poobah of All Things Medical—Hippocrates who named it after the Greek words for crab." Hippocrates, www.egs.edu/library/hippocrates/biography

"He wrote of both prevention and cures for disease, of eating will and exercising, of good personal hygiene and experiment on animals and humans." Celsus, Aulus Cornelius, DeMedicina: In Three Volumes, Cambridge, Mass.: Harvard University Print, 1971

"After excision, even when a scar has formed, nonetheless the disease has returned." Celsus, DeMedinina, Book V, Chapter 28, W.G. Spencer, Ed., Harvard University Press, Cambridge, Mass., 1971

Chapter 3

Dwight D. Eisenhower quote—Dwight D. Eisenhower. BrainyQuote. com, Xplore Inc, 2015. http://www.brainyquote.com/quotes/authors/d/dright_d_eisenhower.html, accessed October 9, 2015

George Bernard Shaw quote—Man and Superman, George Bernard Shaw, The University Press, Cambridge Mass., 1903

"The Massachusetts legislature granted a charter in 1811." "History of Mass General" http://www.massgeneral.org/museum/history/default.aspx, accessed October 9, 2015.

All statistics and information come from the American Cancer Society http://www.cancer.org/cancer/lungcancer/index, accessed October 2015.

"Warning labels didn't come out on cigarettes in the US until 1966." From the Surgeon General (Federal gov't) https://wikipedia.org/wiki/History_ofwarning_labels_intheUS

President Nixon's "War of Cancer"—National Cancer Act of 1971 (Senate Bill 1828—Enacted December 23, 1971) From Office of Government & Congressional Relations. www.Legislative.cancer.gov/history/phsa/1971

Biopsy Risks http://www.online-medical-dictionary.org/ and http://www.hopkinsmedicine.org/healthlibrary/test_procedures/pulmonary/lung_biopsy_92,P07750/

"Cancer is further staged by subcategories of numbers and more letters." The explanation of the breakdown of the diagnosis was based on information from http://www.cancer.org/cancer/lungcancer-non-smallcell/detailedguide/non-small-cell-lung-cancer-staging

"First known cancer statistics." Global Perspectives on Cancer, Kenneth D. Miller and Miklos Senon, Editors, Praeger, 2015, p. 101

Life expectancy information: Max Roser (2015) "Life Expectancy" Published online at OurWorlkInData.org. Retrieved from: http://ourworlkindata.org/data/poplulation-growth-vital-statistics/life-expectancy/

"A medical report from 1912 found only 374 cases of lung cancer mentioned in international medical articles." AT.Henrici, Journal of Medical Research, July, 1912, XXVI, p. 395

The American Cancer Society estimated lung cancer cases in the United States. Cancer Facts and Statistics, American Cancer Society Website: www.cancer.org/research/cancerfactsstatistics

"The National Cancer Institute spends roughly $4.9 billion a year." National Cancer Institute: Comprehensive Cancer Information, www.cancer.gov

Breast cancer survival rates—Breast Cancer Statistics, www.cancer.net/cancer-types/breast-cancer/statistics

USA Today report—www.usatoday.com/story/money (2014/03/24)

Chapter 4

John Wayne quote—www.brainyquotes/quotes/authors/john_wayne.html

Information about the emerald necklace—www.fredericklawolmsted.com/bioframe.html

Christian Register—Channing, Storer, Richardson and the Lying in Hospital, Chaper XVII, page 147.

Brigham and Women's history—www.brighamandwomens.org/ heritage Chapters in American Obstetrics, Vol. 479, Page 147 www. brighamandwomens.org/about_bwh/about_us.aspx

Chapter 5

Rocky Balboa quote—https://goodreads.com/work/quotes/rockybalboa Marilyn Monroe quote—www.goodreads.com/quotes/8630

Chapter 6

Paulo Coelho quote—www.brainyquote.com/quotes/authors/p/ paulo_coelho.html
Kahlil Gibran quote—www.brainyquote.com/quotes/authors/k/ khalil_gibran.html

"Chemotherapy was coined by German chemist, Paul Erlich" www. nobelprize.org/nobel_prizes/1908/Ehrlich-bio.html

"The Father of Modern Chemotherapy." www.dana-farber.org/History-and-milestones.org

"Researchers began focusing on drugs that block different functions in cell growth." www.ncbi.nlm.nih.gov/pubmed/16803563sidneyfarber

"Twenty percent of lung cancer patients." Cancer facts and Statistics, American Cancer Society Website. www.cancer.org/research/ cancerfactstatistice/

Chapter 7

Thomas   Paine   quote—www.brainyquote.com/quotes/authors/t/
thomas_paine.html
Mahatma   Gandhi   quote—www.brainyquote.com/quotes/authors/m/
mahatma_gandhi.html

"Cisplatin has been nicknamed 'Cis-flatten' by nurses." NCI "The
Accidental Cure—Platinum-based Treatment for Cancer: The Discovery
of Cisplatin" www.cancer.gov/research/progress/discovery
20008 by American Society of Clinical Oncology "First-Line Chemotherapy
for Non-small Cell Lung Cancer: Is there a Superior Regimen Based on
History?" By Lawrence Einhorn

"A recent study cited in the Journal of National Cancer Institute."
Oxfordjournals.org/content/95/17/1350.full

"George Herman Ruth was one of the earliest pioneers in chemotherapy."
*The Big Bam: The Life and Times of Babe Ruth, Leigh Montvale, Doubleday,
2005*

http://www.pbs.org/newshour/updates/august-16-1948-babe-ruth-
americas-greatest-baseball-star-pioneer-modern-treatment-cancer-dies/

www.baberuth.com/biography

Chapter 8

Coco Chanel quote—www.goodreads.com/quotes/708175

Elisha Bible story—2 Kings 2:23–34 (King James Version)

If You Knew My Story Lyrics BRIGHT STAR

Song from the Broadway Musical (2016)
Bright Star the musical - If You Knew My Story Lyrics

Original song 'If You Knew My Story' performed by Carmen Cusack (Alice) from the Broadway musical Bright Star.

If you knew my story you'd have a hard time
Believing me, you'd think I was lying
Joy and sorrow never last
I'll die trying not to live in the past
If you knew my story
My heaven and my hell
If you knew my story
You'd have a good story to tell
I left my clothes on that cold river rock
My cares and my woes rolled up in my socks
I lay down in that mountain stream
And the icy water rushed over me
If you knew my story
My heaven and my hell
If you knew my story
You'd have a good story to tell
Me I'm not alone
Tell me I'm not alone
Many backs have broken from lesser weight I know
I was born to carry more than I can hold
Even though I'll stumble
Even though I'll fall
You'll never see me crumble
You'll never see me crawl
If you knew my story
To the water from my well
If you knew my story

You'd have a good story to tell
Me I'm not alone
Tell me I'm not alone
Even though I'll stumble
Even though I'll fall
You'll never see me crumble
You'll never see me crawl
If you knew my story

About the Author

Karen Van de Water is a graduate of Oregon State University with a degree in Health and Human Sciences. She is a Realtor and is a lung cancer survivor. She lives with her two daughters outside of Boston, Massachusetts. Please visit Karen at TheCancerCard.support.

CPSIA information can be obtained
at www.ICGtesting.com
Printed in the USA
LVOW11s1754081216

516411LV00002B/434/P

9 781483 454962